# CHILDCRAFT

## HOLIDAYS AND FAMOUS PEOPLE

# CHILDCRAFT
## IN · FOURTEEN · VOLUMES

### VOLUME SIX

## HOLIDAYS AND FAMOUS PEOPLE

# THE QUARRIE CORPORATION
## CHICAGO

# CHILDCRAFT

# CONTENTS

[See Volume Three, pages vii and viii, for acknowledgments to publishers for copyrighted material used in Volumes Three, Four, Five, and Six. Alphabetical indexes of authors and titles appear at the back of Volume Six.]

## HOLIDAYS AND FESTIVALS

## GLIMPSES OF FAMOUS PEOPLE

## BIBLE STORIES

HOLIDAYS AND FESTIVALS

# Tiny Tim

THE Cratchit family were very poor, for Bob Cratchit, the father, earned scarcely enough to keep his family. But it was Christmas Day, and poor as they were, they were going to have a merry Christmas.

Mrs. Cratchit laid the cloth, assisted by Belinda Cratchit, second of her daughters; while Master Peter Cratchit blew the fire, until the slow potatoes, bubbling up, knocked loudly at the saucepan lid to be let out and peeled. Two smaller Cratchits, boy and girl, came tearing in, screaming that outside the baker's they had smelt the goose, and known it for their own. Then Martha, the eldest daughter, who worked for a milliner, came home, and last of all in came Bob, the father, with at least three feet of comforter, besides the fringe, hanging down before him, with his threadbare clothes darned and brushed to look seasonable, and with Tiny Tim on his shoulder. Alas for Tiny Tim! He bore always a little crutch and had his limbs supported by an iron frame.

The two young Cratchits hustled Tiny Tim off to the washhouse, that he might hear the pudding singing in the copper.

"And how did little Tim behave?" asked Mother Cratchit.

"As good as gold," said Bob, "and better. He told me coming home that he hoped the people saw him in the church, because he was a cripple, and it might be pleasant for them to remember, upon Christmas Day, Who made lame beggars walk and blind men see."

Bob's voice trembled, and it trembled more when he said that he thought Tiny Tim was growing strong and hearty.

But they heard the sound of Tiny Tim's little crutch upon the floor and they helped him over to his stool by the fire. Master Peter and the two young Cratchits went out to the baker's to fetch the goose, and when it came there was such a bustle that you might have thought

a goose the rarest of all birds. Mother Cratchit made the gravy (ready before in a little saucepan) hissing hot; Peter mashed the potatoes; Belinda sweetened the applesauce; Martha dusted the hot plates; Bob placed Tiny Tim beside him at one corner of the table; and the two little Cratchits set chairs for everybody, cramming spoons in their mouths lest they should shriek for goose before it came their turn to be served.

There never was such a goose! Bob said he didn't believe there ever was such a goose cooked. With the applesauce and the mashed potatoes there was enough dinner for the whole family. Indeed, Mother Cratchit said, as they looked at one small piece of a bone upon the dish, that they hadn't eaten it all, at last. Yet everyone had

enough and the little Cratchits were steeped in sage and onion to the eyebrows.  Now Belinda changed the plates and Mother Cratchit left the room, alone, to take up the pudding and bring it in.

Suppose it should not be done enough!  Suppose it should break!  Suppose somebody had come over the back wall and stolen it while they were making merry with the goose!

Hello!  A great deal of steam!  The pudding was out of the copper.  A smell like a washing day!  That was the cloth.  A smell like an eating house and a pastry cook's next door to each other, with a laundress's next door to that!  That was the pudding!  In half a minute Mother Cratchit entered with the pudding like a speckled cannon ball, so hard and firm, and blazing, and bedight with Christmas holly stuck into the top! Everybody had something to say about it, but nobody thought it at all a small pudding for a large family. Any Cratchit would have blushed to hint at such a thing.

At last the dinner was all done, the cloth was cleared, the hearth swept, and the fire made up. Apples and oranges were put upon the table, and a shovelful of chestnuts upon the fire, where they began to sputter and crack noisily. Then all the Cratchit family drew around the hearth. Tiny Tim sat very close to his father's side upon his little stool. Bob held his withered little hand in his, for he loved the child, and wished to keep him by his side, as if he feared that he might be taken from him.

"A merry Christmas to us all, my dears; God bless us!" said Bob Cratchit.

"Merry Christmas! Merry Christmas!" said all the Cratchit family.

"God bless us—every one!" said Tiny Tim, the last of all.

Adapted from CHARLES DICKENS, *A Christmas Carol*

 *Christmas*

I FEEL as though tomorrow morning would never, never come," said Nancy.

It was the night before Christmas, and her mother had just smoothed the covers over her as she lay in bed and had kissed her good night.

"Well, don't wake too soon," said Mrs. Rutledge, smiling; "that is all I ask."

Then she lowered the gas until it was only a point of light, and went into her own room to finish the last of her Christmas preparations. Nancy heard her stirring about there, and some papers rustled. She wondered whether it was a present for her that her mother was unwrapping. So many, many hours it would be before morning, and she felt as though she would never go to sleep.

She began to repeat in her mind "The Night before Christmas." Her father had read it aloud that evening, as he always did on Christmas Eve. Presently her thoughts wandered.

"The stockings were hung by the chimney with care——"

It seemed to be Aunt Hannah who was hanging them up, only it was a row of black flannel cats. Then Dick was there and was telling her about a little sleigh he had found in the tool house, and from these dreams Nancy drifted into deeper and deeper sleep.

Later on her father and mother came upstairs and into her room without disturbing her. They stole softly about, moving and arranging things. A table was cleared and put nearer to her bed, and on it was placed something large and square, something so large that there was no room on the table for anything else. It was one of her Christmas presents.

Her father smiled to himself. "I should like to see her face when she first sees it," he whispered.

Her mother smiled, too, and nodded. "We'll put the rest of the things at the foot of the bed," she said, and placed there Nancy's other Christmas gifts, large and small.

Then, when everything was arranged, she and Mr. Rutledge stole away again, and all the while the little girl never stirred in her sleep.

It was Dick who awoke her at last—many, many hours later, when morning had come. "Merry Christmas! Merry Christmas!" he was shouting.

"Merry Christmas!" answered voices from the other rooms.

Nancy opened her eyes. For a moment she could not think what it was all about. Then she remembered. It was Christmas at last. "Merry Christmas!" she cried, starting up in bed.

Suddenly her eyes fell on the table and the Christmas present on it. "Oh," she exclaimed, and then again, "Oh! It is! Oh, Dick, they've given me that little house Father made for Gladys."

She heard Dick laugh. "No, they haven't."

"But they have. It's here, and it says, 'For Nancy, from Father and Mother.'"

"I know, but it's another house. Father made it in the evenings after you were in bed, and they gave the one you saw to Cousin Gladys."

However, there stood a little house, and so like the other that

Nancy could not have told them apart. The shining windows and shingled roof, the green palings enclosing the lawn, the little pond, the swan with arching neck—everything was there, even to the little pot of flowers on each side of the door. It all seemed more fascinating than ever.

"Don't stand about in your bare feet, Nancy," called her mother, and the little girl, who had slipped from bed to examine the house more closely, scrambled back again.

Then she saw the packages heaped at the foot of the bed, and eagerly she began to unwrap and examine them. There was a box of puzzle blocks from Oscar, a little purse with bright pennies in it from Tom, and a china vase from Dick. Her Aunt Clara had sent her a book, and her cousins, a music box.

But the best thing of all, next to the little house, was the present from Aunt Anna. It was the cunningest little doll's trunk that Nancy had ever seen, and it had a lock and key and a tray just like a real trunk. How glad she was that she had said she wanted Gladys to have the doll's house, even before she knew she was to have one like it!

Meanwhile she could hear Dick rustling paper and snapping string in his own room, and he and she kept calling to each other about their presents.

"Skates!" cried Dick. "Just exactly what I wanted.—And a new knife!" Then presently, in a surprised tone, "Why, here's a cap just like the one I lost!"

Nancy gave a little bounce of excitement. "That's from me, but I forgot to write on it. Aren't you surprised? Isn't it just like your other? Just exactly?"

"It's fine; thank you, Nance," said Dick. She knew how pleased he must be when he called her "Nance."

When the children had looked at all their presents and emptied their stockings, it was time to dress.

Oscar was whistling gaily in his room, and Tom was trying on the new fur gloves that were a present from his father.

It was quite late when they all gathered at the breakfast table, but then that was expected on Christmas morning. Mr. Rutledge was wearing his new watch guard that Nancy and Dick had given him, and Mrs. Rutledge said she was delighted with the thimble they had given her. Tom and Oscar were pleased with their gifts, too.

"And the Christmas tree still remains to be seen," reminded Mrs. Rutledge.

The Christmas tree! They had almost forgotten that in the excitement of the presents. And yet, when later on they gathered about it in the library, how beautiful it was! The boughs were gay with cornucopias and colored chains; the glittering ornaments shone and quivered, and from the topmost spray, with lifted hands and golden wings, hung a Christmas angel.

While they were all standing round and admiring it, there was a ring at the doorbell, and Rachel came running in. At the door she stopped short. "Oh! Oh!" she cried.

"This is our Christmas tree," said Nancy. "Isn't it lovely?"

"Oh, it is." She stood staring at it with shining eyes. "We didn't have one at our house."

"Then this one shall be partly yours, and you must come over and see it whenever you can," said Mrs. Rutledge.

Suddenly Rachel remembered what she had come over for. "Here's a present for you, Nancy. Merry Christmas!" she said, and put a little package, neatly wrapped and tied with ribbon, into Nancy's hand.

"What is it? I wonder what it is!" cried Nancy. But when she unwrapped it, and saw the little doll in the bathtub, she was overcome with admiration. "Why, Rachel! I think it's the sweetest thing I ever saw. Just look, Mother!"

She had a present for Rachel, too. It was a gay red and gold pencil with a lead point that would screw out and in, and Rachel seemed almost as delighted with it as Nancy was with her present.

After a while the children got down on the floor and began to fit the puzzle blocks together. Then they took out their last year's toy farm, and set the animals out on the floor, and laid out little fields with fences and trees. Nancy's new house was the city house. The dolls lived there and sent over to the farm for milk and eggs. The children made little balls of wax and put them under a plaster hen for "pretend eggs." How pleasant it all was!

Gladys came in for a while to see the presents and to show the new wax doll her mother had given her. She thanked Mrs. Rutledge for the little house, and said how pretty it was, but she was not more delighted with it than Nancy was with hers. Sarah and little Esther came in, too, but none of the children stayed long.

At dinnertime Rachel was the only visitor who was still there. Mrs. Rutledge came to the library door. "Can't you stay and have dinner with us, Rachel?" she asked.

"I don't know!"

"Wouldn't you like to run over home and ask your father whether you might?"

Rachel bent her head low over the little sheep she was moving about. "Oh, he said I might—that is, if you asked me—if I was home by five o'clock. We don't have dinner till five."

"Oh, good! I'm so glad!" cried Nancy.

So Rachel stayed, and after dinner they played again, and Dick played with them until five o'clock, when she had to go.

But almost the best time of the whole day was the evening, when the family gathered around the lighted lamp, and Mrs. Rutledge read aloud from one of the new books that had been given them.

When Nancy was in bed that night and her mother stooped to give her her good-night kiss, the little girl reached up and put her arms about her mother's neck, holding her tight. "Oh, hasn't it been a lovely day!" she said. "I wish tomorrow was Christmas all over again, don't you?"

But much as Mrs. Rutledge had enjoyed it all, she could hardly agree to that. She said she thought that one Christmas a year was enough.

KATHARINE PYLE, from *Nancy Rutledge*

# A Valentine Story

LONG ago, there lived in a faraway country two boys. These boys were just like boys today because they liked to play. But the people who lived near did not like to hear the noise they made when they were having their good times.

Once when they were playing a new game, a messenger left them a note which said,

"You will not be allowed to play on the street any more. If you do, you will be punished."

This made the two boys unhappy.

Then Benedict, the older boy, told Julius that they would take the note to their friend Valentine, an old man who lived in a house with a large garden. Valentine loved children and was always kind to them. When he read the note, he smiled and said,

"You may come into my garden and play. I am sure no one will stop you there."

Every day the boys walked quietly down the street. But the min-

ute they were inside the garden wall they could run and shout as much as they pleased.

One day the boys went to the garden and found the gate locked. No one answered when they knocked. They waited and waited. Then they went home and tried to be quiet, but it was very hard.

The boys had not heard about Valentine. They did not know that the King had sent him to prison for the rest of his life. Valentine was wondering how he could send the boys the key to the garden gate. At last he thought of a plan.

One day the boys were looking out of the window. They were unhappy because they could not run and play. Suddenly a white pigeon flew down to the window sill. Around the pigeon's leg a key and a note were tied. Benedict held the pigeon gently while Julius untied the key and the note.

The note read,

"This key will open the garden gate for two boys I love."

Then the boys were happy because they knew that Valentine remembered them.

As the boys grew older, they learned that Valentine had sent messages to all his friends. This is why people send messages of love on Valentine's birthday. This is why the fourteenth of February is called Saint Valentine's Day.

EVELYN DAVIS

# The Twig That Became a Tree

### A STORY FOR ARBOR DAY

THE tree of which I am about to tell you was once a little twig. There were many others like it, and the farmer came to look at them every day, to see if they were all doing well.

By and by he began to take away the older and stronger twigs, and one day he dug up this little tree and carried it away to an open field.

There its roots were again put into the soft, warm ground, and it held its pretty head up as if looking into the blue sky. Just at sunset the farmer's wife came out to look at the new tree.

"I wonder if I shall ever see apples growing on these twigs," she said to herself.

The little tree heard it, and said softly, "We shall see! Come, gentle rain and warm sun, and let me be the first to give a fine, red apple to the farmer's wife."

And the rain and the sun did come, and the branches grew, and the roots dug deep into the soft ground, and at last, one bright spring day, the farmer's wife cried,

"Just see! One of our little trees has some blossoms on it! I believe that, young and small as it is, that tree will give me an apple this autumn."

But the farmer laughed and said, "Oh, it is not old enough to bear apples yet."

The little tree said nothing, but all to itself it thought, "The good woman shall have an apple this very year."

And she did. When the cool days of autumn came, and the leaves began to fade and grow yellow, two red apples hung upon one of the branches of the tree.

## Jack-o'-Lantern

HALLOWEEN was coming. Peggy liked Halloween best of all the days except Christmas. So did Betty, Ned, and Dick. Ned and Dick lived near Peggy. They were in her class at school. They planned to have fun in school that day. They told the other children of their plans. They called it a Jack-o'-Lantern party.

All the children made costumes. The girls made their costumes of yellow cloth. The boys made their costumes of black paper.

The girls cut out black cats and witches and sewed them on their costumes. The boys cut out yellow pumpkins and pasted them on their costumes.

They all made paper caps. Some caps were black and some caps were yellow.

When they put on their costumes, the children looked like jolly pumpkins.

The day came and every child brought a Jack-o'-Lantern to school. There were twenty children in the class.

Miss White, the teacher, pulled down the dark shades. The room was very dark and still.

Miss White said, "Watch and you will see the Jack-o'-Lanterns laughing at you."

Sure enough, first Peggy's Jack began to grin, then Betty's.

One by one, every Jack was laughing at the children. Of course the children laughed back at the Jacks.

There were forty-one laughing faces in the classroom that day.

Then Peggy hid in a dark corner of the room. The children did not see her.

A voice seemed to come from Peggy's Jack-o'-Lantern. This is what he said:

Oh, once I was a pumpkin yellow,
Now I am a jolly fellow.

On Halloween I skip and prance
And join the witches in the dance.

With broomstick nag I speed on high,
And turn a somersault in the sky.

Then down I come with mighty thump
And make the silly earth folks jump.

I play with goblins hide and seek,
And pull their caps and make them squeak.

I fly up to the moon and sing
With cats so black in magic ring.

I peep into your windows bright
And grin at you for your delight.

All night I skip and shout and play;
When morning comes I'm far away.

All the children clapped and said, "Oh, say it again!"

The other Jacks seemed to like to hear their brother talk. They looked very jolly.

Betty said, "Let us teach all our Jacks to say it."

Peggy gave each of them a copy of the rhyme to take home.

Then all the Jack-o'-Lanterns and children went home for more Halloween fun.

MILDRED BATCHELDER, from *Peggy Stories*

# A Halloween Surprise

LITTLE Mrs. Dingle lived alone at the far end of the town. She lived in a small brown cottage, with a large yard and garden. There she grew cabbages, corn, and other vegetables, but she had to work hard to get enough to eat.

Mrs. Dingle was a timid little old lady. She was afraid of boys. She had no sons of her own. On Halloween she was especially afraid that the boys of the neighborhood would play tricks on her.

Sometimes they did play tricks on her. They came to her house and rang her bell. They carried off her gate and left it in a field far down the road. She had to pay a man to bring it back for her, as it was too heavy for her to carry. When the gate was off, cows and pigs would stray in and eat up her vegetables.

One day as she was frying doughnuts and baking pumpkin pies she remembered that that night would be Halloween. It was the pumpkin that reminded her. She had no pumpkins in her garden, but a neighbor had brought her some in a dish, and said,

"Make yourself some nice pumpkin pies for Halloween. I have given the boys the shells to make lanterns of."

So little Mrs. Dingle remembered and was frightened. She wondered what the boys would do to her.

When evening came, she took in all her brooms and her mop and pails. She was afraid the boys would hide those as they had done before.

After a while she heard the boys shouting and clattering down the street. Then they were still, and she thought they were hiding and waiting their chance to come near and do all the mischief they could. She looked out to see whether her gate was safe. When she saw it swinging open in the moonlight, she knew that the boys had come in and must be somewhere about the yard. She had closed the gate very carefully before dark. She looked through the window a long time, but nothing happened.

At last she thought she heard a sound of chopping at the back of the house. She ran to the kitchen window. There she saw dark figures moving about. She must have forgotten to lock the wood-shed door. There was a light inside and the sound of chopping seemed to come from there, although the door was closed.

She returned to the front window. The gate was still on its hinges, but she saw several dark figures moving about. She could not tell what they were doing. She wanted to know, but she could not make up her mind to go out and see. But at last, as the noise continued, she took courage, and putting a shawl over her head, went to the woodshed.

As she opened the back door, she heard a shrill whistle. The light went out in the woodshed, and the noise stopped.

She returned to the kitchen, lighted a lantern, and went out again. As she opened the woodshed door and held up her light, the first thing she saw was a great pile of chopped wood. The next was a great pile of dry twigs for lighting fires. The third was the face of a boy hiding behind it.

"Come out," said the old woman, "and tell me what you've been up to."

Nobody came out and nobody answered, but there was a giggle, then another, until all over the woodshed somebody seemed to be giggling.

Mrs. Dingle stood at the door and held up her lantern. She could not see any boys outside, but she saw that the grass between the shed

and the house had been raked clean of leaves. She had been meaning for a week to rake them away, but was stiff with rheumatism. Then she turned and looked at the great pile of wood, and remembered how many times she had had backache from chopping wood. Then she saw what the boys had been up to.

She said loudly, "I have some work for any boy who comes to the kitchen."

She went away. No one answered, but she heard whispers and giggles behind her.

She went to her pantry and got down the great stone jar of doughnuts. She did not have long to wait. In a minute the kitchen seemed to be full of boys. There might have been eight or ten of them—I don't know. She gave each of them two doughnuts, and then she cut up two of her pumpkin pies for them.

And when they went away, one of them carefully shut the gate behind them.

If you ask me how the boys came to think of such a Halloween surprise, I shall have to say that I don't know. For, you see, the story really happened, and if the boys ever told anyone, they did not tell me.

NINA LEUBRIE

# Thanksgiving Day of 1779

THIS year it was Uncle Simeon's turn to have the dinner at his house, but of course we all helped them as they help us when it is our turn, and there is always enough for us all to do. The baking of pies and cakes was done at our house, and we had the big oven heated and filled twice a day for three days before it was all done. Everything was *good,* though we did have to do without some things that ought to be used. Neither love nor money could buy raisins, but our red cherries dried without the pits did almost as well, and happily Uncle Simeon still had some spices in store.

The tables were set in the dining hall, and even that big room had no space to spare when we were all seated. The servants had enough ado to get around the tables and serve us without upsetting things. There were our two grandmothers side by side. They are always handsome old ladies, but now, many thought, they were handsomer than ever, and happy they were to look around upon so many of their descendants. Uncle and Aunt Simeon presided at one table, and Father and Mother at the other.

Of course we could have no roast beef. None of us has tasted beef this three years back, as it must go to the army, and too little they get, poor fellows. But Nayquittymaw's hunters were able to get us a fine red deer, so that we had a haunch of venison on each table. Each was balanced by a huge chine of roast pork at the other end of the table. Then there was on one, a big roast turkey, and on the other, a goose and two big pigeon pastries.

There was also an abundance of vegetables of the old sorts and one which I do not believe you have yet seen. Uncle Simeon had imported the seed from England just before the war began, and only this year was there enough for table use. It is called celery, and you eat it without cooking. It is very good, served with meats. Next year Uncle Simeon says he will be able to raise enough to give us all some. It has to be taken up, roots and all, and buried in earth in the cellar through the winter. You pull it up only when you want to use it.

Our mince pies were good, although we had to use dried cherries, as I told you, and the meat was haunch of venison instead of beef. The pumpkin pies, apple tarts, and big Indian puddings lacked nothing save appetites by the time we had got round to them.

There was no plum pudding, but a boiled suet pudding, stirred thick with dried plums and cherries, was called by the old name, and answered the purpose. All the other spices had been used in the mince pies, and so for this pudding we used a jar of West India preserved ginger which chanced to be left of the last shipment which Uncle Simeon had from there. We chopped the ginger small and stirred it through with the plums and cherries. It was *extraordinarily* good.

The day was bitter cold, and when we got home from meeting, which Father did not keep overlong by reason of the cold, we were glad enough of the fire in Uncle's dining hall. But by the time dinner was half over, those of us who were on the fire side of one table were forced to get up and carry our plates with us around to the far side of the other table, while those who had sat there were as glad to bring their plates around to the fire side to get warm. The old ladies had a screen put to their chairs.

Uncle Simeon was in his best mood, and you know how good that is. He kept both tables in a roar of laughter with his droll stories of the days when he was studying medicine in Edinburgh. Afterward, he and Father and Uncle Paul joined in singing hymns and ballads. You know how finely their voices go together. Then we all sang a hymn, and my dear father led us in prayer, remembering the absent friends. Much I wished that my dear Betsey were here as one of us, as she had been in days of yore.

We did not rise from the table until it was quite dark. Then when the dishes had been cleared away, we got round the fire as close as we could and cracked nuts and sang songs and told stories. At least some told and others listened. You know nobody can exceed the two grandmothers at telling tales of the things they have seen themselves, and repeating those of the early years in New England, which they had heard in their youth from their elders. My father says it is a goodly custom to hand down all worthy deeds and traditions from father to son, as the Israelites were commanded to do about the Passover, and as the Indians here have always done, because the spoken word is remembered longer than the written word.

Brother Jack did not reach here until late on Wednesday, though he had left college early on Monday morning and had ridden with all due diligence, considering the snow. He brought an orange to each of the grandmothers, but alas! they were frozen in his saddlebags. We soaked the frost out in cold water, but I fear they weren't as good as they should have been.

Adapted from HELEN EVERTSON SMITH,
*An Old Time Thanksgiving*

# A Long-Ago Thanksgiving

LITTLE Josephine Dillard sat up very straight on the back seat of the family carriage, her doll Marietta in her lap. She was a slim little girl with dark hair that was almost short. Her doll had fair china hair and bright red cheeks. With her father and mother she was going to spend Thanksgiving with Uncle Eben and Aunt Prudence, who lived on the other side of Little River. Aunt Prudence had written that if the spice cake held out, there would be a small party in the evening with two little girls from down the road for company. Whenever Jo thought of the party she gave a bounce. In those simple days parties were very rare; Jo had never had one.

There had been long rains, and Ned and Sally, the horses, had to travel very slowly. Their long tails were stiff with mud.

Now and then Jo glanced down at a box in the foot of the carriage. In that box were two best dresses—a plain dark red worsted of her own and a dark blue worsted of Marietta's. They were the only two dresses that she and Marietta owned in the world besides the two that they were wearing; they were their party dresses.

All at once a strange thing happened. They had come to Little River, and it looked strangely deep. Mr. Dillard pulled the horses to a standstill and peered first at the foaming water, then at the road.

"Well," he said at last, "I can see from the tracks that other people have been in."

So in they went, too. But right away they saw their mistake. The water had risen a great deal since the last vehicle crossed. Down, down

went the wheels, the horses plunged and splashed. The carriage began to tip, and all at once muddy water was pouring all over them.

Father guided the horses, and Mother grasped Jo, and Jo held fast to Marietta. It was all very bad while it lasted but in a little while the carriage righted itself, and the faithful horses pulled them safely to the other side.

"Well, we have more than ever to be thankful for," Jo's father said, when he could say anything at all.

They were all three dripping and bedraggled, like three ducks who had been out too long in the rain.

"My," Jo gasped, shaking the water out of her hair, "I'm glad those party dresses are well wrapped up!" She reached for the box. Then— "O Mother," she cried in a weak little voice, "the box has been washed away!"

It was only too true. Though Mother tried hard to comfort her, for a time Jo felt that she could not bear it. But at last, with a big effort, she choked back the tears. All the rest of the way, though, she kept saying to herself, "There'll be nothing to wear to the party."

At last, cold and covered with mud, they reached Uncle Eben's house.

"Well, well!" said kind Aunt Prudence, as she lifted the forlorn little girl from the carriage and heard the sad tale. "Never you mind. My cousin's little boy, Tommy Brown, left some of his clothes here for me to mend, and into those we'll pop you right away, as warm as toast."

Jo's heart sank. Was it possible that she was going to be put into a boy's clothes? Then she said to herself that Father and Mother would probably have to put on some one else's clothes, too, and *they* were not making any fuss. But oh, if Tommy Brown had only been a girl!

An hour later a queer-looking little figure, dressed in a loose brown coat and baggy brown trousers, sat huddled in the chimney corner, as far out of sight as possible. This was a strange Thanksgiving Day, Jo thought, miserably. She wished she could change places with muddy Marietta, hidden upstairs in the spare-room closet.

Aunt Prudence was saying that it was a mercy they had reached there at all. There had never been such autumn rains. The girl who helped her in the kitchen had been kept away by the high water. Aunt Prudence had to keep on jumping up and going into the kitchen, for with no help, there was of course much to do. After a while Mother went in to help her.

In the great fireplace the red flames flickered and made shadows on the wall; Father and Uncle Eben talked on and on about crops. Jo began to fidget. She knew that she ought to be helping in the kitchen, but she was ashamed to walk across the floor in her funny clothes.

"I could set the table," she kept thinking. "And pare the potatoes."

After a while she got up without making any sound and crept softly out of her corner and into the kitchen. There were so many jobs waiting there for her that soon she was working for dear life.

All at once came the second strange happening of that strange day. Out in the yard horses stamped and harness jingled; then there was a quick, loud knock at the door.

In a flash poor Jo remembered Tommy Brown's baggy trousers. She started to make a dash for the stairs, but just as she got halfway through the living room, Uncle Eben led in three strangers—a tall man, a lady, and a little golden-haired girl with a doll. At sight of that little girl Jo forgot, for a minute, all about Tommy Brown's trousers.

There was a flurry in the farmhouse when the family found out who the strangers were. The tall man was the Governor of the state. He and his wife and daughter, on their way to the city, had been turned back by the high water. Could they stay at Uncle Eben's house, he asked, until a few hours later, when fresh horses would be brought to take them by another road?

Of course they were most welcome. As Aunt Prudence hurried off to make more biscuits she whispered to Jo, "Set three more places at the table."

"O *dear!*" Jo thought. "If I could only go upstairs." But how could she leave Aunt Prudence with a Governor's family to care for? She glanced at the little girl.

The newcomer smiled. "What is your name?" she asked. "Mine's Melissa, and my doll's is Flora."

"Mine's Jo," was the hasty answer. Then, without another look,

Jo fled to the kitchen. But now and then as she worked, she stole back to peep at Melissa, who sat lonesomely rocking her doll before the fire.

When it was dinnertime at last, Jo was glad to wait on the table instead of sitting down with the rest. She would not look at Melissa, but once, as she paused at the Governor's elbow with the potatoes, he glanced down at her with a twinkle.

"Well, Jo," he said, "I think you are the most useful lad I ever saw."

The two Dillard families looked surprised at that; they had been too busy to remember Jo's strange clothes. But, to her great relief, no one said anything.

When dinner was over and the dishes washed, a weary little girl stole tiptoe up to the spare room, where another fire had been lighted. She took off Marietta's poor muddy dress and hung it by the fire; then she sat down to rock her. It was cozy by the fire, and she almost went to sleep.

Suddenly there was a stir at the door. "Little boy," a small voice said wistfully, "don't you ever play at all?"

Jo sat up blinking. She tried to stuff Marietta under the edge of her coat, but it was too late.

"A doll!" cried the Governor's little girl, her blue eyes opening wide. "I *didn't* know boys ever played with dolls!"

This was too much. Marietta slipped to the floor unheeded, and poor Jo bowed over in the chair, her face in her hands.

Melissa hurried across the room and picked up the doll. Then she laid a hand on the bowed head. "Don't cry," she begged. "Please, little boy, don't cry."

At that Jo lifted her wet face. "I'm not a little b-b-boy," she sobbed. "I am just as much a little g-g-girl as you are!"

Then, of course, the whole story came out. It didn't take long to tell, and soon Jo and Melissa were playing away as happily as though they had always known each other.

"I wish you could stay to my party," Jo said at last. "O, no," she added, laughing. "There won't be any. I forgot about Tommy's trousers. All the same, though, playing with you and Flora has been nicer than any party."

But Melissa was troubled at the thought of her new friend's disappointment; she kept thinking about it.

After a while the Governor's wife came up to tell her little girl it was time to go. As they put on their wraps, Jo, bashful again, went softly downstairs and tucked herself away once more in her chimney corner. The old clock in the corner seemed to be making a happy ticking; it had sounded so doleful before dinner.

It seemed to her that Melissa and her mother were a long time getting into their things. There was much bustling and whispering; and once she saw the Governor's driver carrying a box upstairs.

"Come!" she heard the Governor calling at last. "We must be gone."

Then Melissa came tripping in to look for Jo. "Think of me at the party tonight," she said, as she kissed the funny little figure good-by.

Jo wondered what made her say that. She stood at the window till the carriage was out of sight. As she turned back to the fire, her mother said, "There's something out in the hall that the Governor's little girl left for you."

On the old chest in the hall Jo found a flat white box. Wondering, she brought it in and opened it. Inside, lay a lovely little pink silk dress covered with flounces, and under that a very tiny blue silk dress, made in the same way. On the card she read, "For Jo and Marietta, from Melissa and Flora, to be worn at the party."

Jo could not speak; she could only dance up and down.

"Well, it's a good thing I made an extra little cake at the last minute," Aunt Prudence said, smiling. "And some extra apple sauce. There'll be a-plenty for the party."

Jo went racing up the old dark stairs and ran into the spare room. "O Marietta, my child," she cried, as she picked up the muddy little doll and poked the fire till it burned up brightly. *"Such* a Thanksgiving day! Just look and see what I have in this box!"

NANCY BYRD TURNER

# The Prettiest Valentine

THE table in the breakfast room at Betty Sue's house was gay with colored papers, ribbons, pictures, paints, and crayons. Betty Sue and Sally Lou were making valentines. This afternoon they were working hard, for the teacher had announced a prize contest. The child making the prettiest valentine all by herself would receive a prize. This was Wednesday. On Friday the valentines would be placed on exhibit, and the children would vote for their choice.

Sally Lou and Betty Sue were very much excited. A dozen ideas had popped in and out of each little head, but at last each had decided on her plans. Sally Lou wanted a very gay valentine. So she cut a cardboard heart, and covered it with scarlet satin. Over this was to be placed a smaller white heart, with a little swinging door cut in the center. When you opened the door, there would be a Cupid throwing kisses to you. Sally was trying to paint red hearts and transfer Cupids onto her white heart. The hearts were rather crooked, and the Cupids all awry, for Sally Lou's fingers were not as nimble as her brain, but she thought it all very lovely. She had made up the nicest verses to go with her valentine. They read:

Cupids One,
Cupids Two,
Cupids Three,
Send love to you.

Betty Sue loved dainty, artistic things. She had decided on a forget-me-not design. There was to be a wreath of forget-me-nots around the edge of a large white heart. She had found the picture of a pretty little girl dancing in a fluffy blue dress, for the center. On the top was to be a blue satin bow. In blue letters she intended to print:

Forget-me-not, My Valentine

Easily, busily, happily, they were working while fat Mrs. Hutton, who cleaned by the day, trudged heavily about the kitchen, singing in a loud voice her favorite song:

"Go tell Aunt Rhoda,
Go tell Aunt Rhoda,
Go tell Aunt Rhoda
Her old grey goose is dead.

"He's worth saving,
He's worth saving,
He's worth saving
To make a feather bed."

"Goodness," whispered Sally Lou, "hasn't she the loudest voice? And does she ever, ever sing anything but that? Every time I am here she sings that."

"Well, I don't know. She yells pretty loud. But she's happy. I'm going to ask her if Grace is making a valentine."

Grace was Mrs. Hutton's little daughter. She was in the girls' room at school, and was the best speller and the neatest writer of all the class. She learned her lessons well and had little to say.

"Mrs. Hutton," asked Betty Sue, when that lady paused for breath in her singing, "is Grace making a valentine for the contest? She draws so nicely."

"O, I dunno," replied the mother. "I never pay any attention to

what she does. I have my work and she has hers. She doesn't like Valentine's day nohow. There ain't no money to buy valentines with, and no funny things like you have to make 'em. It's no fun to sit in school and see some of the girls get 'em by the dozen and only get one or two. Those that gives, gets. Besides, it's her birthday and she wants a party and she can't have none."

"O, that's dreadful," said Sally Lou. "Mrs. Hutton, we have lots more things than we need here. If Grace comes by tonight before you go home, we want to give her part of them and some patterns."

"Yes," chimed in Betty Sue, "she could make lovely valentines. Teacher always sends her to the board when she wants the nicest work done. Why, last Christmas she let her have the whole box of colored chalk to draw Santa and the tree and the presents."

"Did she now?" fat Mrs. Hutton's face was rosy with pride in spite of the fact that she "never paid no attention nohow." She said, "That would be real nice of you girls to help her."

Such a generous pile as the little girls made for Grace! Pretty papers, silver and gold stars, lace paper from candy boxes and different colored ribbons.

"I have an extra box of paints I can give her and a brush," said Betty Sue.

"And I'll run home and get her some crayons and some more pictures," added Sally Lou. "Isn't this fun?"

The pile was just neatly packed in a box, when Grace, as she often did, came by for her mother. She said very little about her gift, but her eyes spoke many things, and as she was leaving she said, "I'll make you girls the very prettiest."

The next morning the chums went to school early and had a long talk with the teacher. Friday morning when Mrs. Hutton came to clean, Betty Sue said: "Please, please, Mrs. Hutton, won't you let Grace wear her best dress to school? The red one she wears to Sunday school? We are all dressing up, and we want her to for a special reason."

Mrs. Hutton was in one of her crossest moods, but she finally agreed with a grunt, and the girls ran singing to school.

Such an excited room of children as there was, when all the lovely valentines were placed in a long row for the voting!

"O, O, O, how can we ever choose among so many beauties?" sighed the children.

But there was really little doubt as to which valentine would get the prize. It was a heart-shaped book. The front page was blue and silver, decorated with flying bluebirds. The next page was pale pink, and on it was drawn and painted such a pretty wild rose.

"The Rose is Red," it said.

On a lavender page was a spray of violets and underneath:

"The Violet's Blue."

A white page showed a little girl eating candy:

"Sugar's Sweet."

And the last page had little red hearts scattered about and ended:

"So are Sally Lou
And Betty Sue."

My! I wish you might have seen Grace's face light up when she was given a prize—a valentine box of heart-shaped candy.

But the joys of that day were not over. When school opened after recess in the afternoon, and the children sat eagerly waiting for the valentine box, the teacher said, "Children, we have a really truly valentine with us today. This is Grace Hutton's birthday, and she shall be postman, and pass out the valentines."

How the children clapped and clapped! And do you know, every child in the room had given Grace a valentine, and some had given her two. Her desk was overflowing. Do you suppose some bluebirds had whispered the secret about the birthday?

Well, after the valentine box was over, Teacher said, "We shall now have the biggest valentine of all. Each of you close your eyes, and put your head on your desk. Don't dare to peak even the least bit until I say you may."

And they heard Teacher bustling about, and pretty soon she counted, "One, two, three, look."

My! There was a big birthday cake with eight red candles burning, and each child had a red candy heart on her piece of cake. And each one had a cone full of pink ice cream, too. The pupils all voted this the nicest kind of a Valentine's day.

As for Grace, can you think how she felt? She had had her long wanted birthday party, and had more valentines than anybody. But best of all, she had been able to give to her friends.

Sally Lou and Betty Sue were also happy. They felt they had had a much nicer day than if either of them had won the prize, though they really each had two rewards. First, they had the reward of having made a little girl completely happy; and, second, they each had a prize valentine. For Grace gave the one on display to Betty Sue, and the one she made for Sally Lou was almost like it. The only difference was that the cover was scarlet and gold, to please gay Sally, and little robin redbreasts were hopping all about it.

RUTH GIPSON PLOWHEAD

## Adventure on the Fourth

W E WOULDN'T have done it, of course, if Mother had told us not to. We very carefully didn't do any of the things she said not to do while she was away. We didn't throw stones for Reginald to chase, and we didn't go out in the boat, and we didn't set off a single firecracker. We very carefully didn't set off any firecrackers, because she told us that three times, and it was the last thing that she called to us from the boat. But she didn't once say, "Don't climb the pine trees."

Of course, Mother wouldn't have deserted us on a holiday except for something very important. It was right after breakfast, and firecrackers were popping all around the lake, when between pops we heard someone shouting and yoohooing on the shore. We looked across and there was Mr. Briggs, who lives on a farm and brings us vegetables and eggs. So Jack rowed across and Mr. Briggs had a telegram for Mother.

"Stationmaster said it came last night," he said, "but there wasn't nobody comin' this way, so he kept it till I drove by. But I never thought you'd hear me with all the cannonadin'."

Jack knew the telegram must be from Daddy because he hadn't come the night before when we were expecting him. Mother read it to us: "Aunt Charlotte in Boston tomorrow only. Hopes to see you."

Aunt Charlotte is our great-aunt and she is very old. She thinks children should be seen and not heard, and when we are noisy she says, "Mercy me!" So we weren't at all happy to think of giving up our Fourth of July on the island to spend the day at a hotel in town trying to be quiet. We told Mother that we'd much rather stay at the lake, and that we would be very trustworthy.

"But Fourth of July!" said Mother, looking worried. "It's such a dangerous day."

"We'll keep out of danger," said Jack.

"We won't leave the island," said Beany.

"We can paint our painting books," I said.

"We-ll," said Mother reluctantly, and she began to get ready, all the time telling us what not to do while she was gone.

"And when Daddy and I come home," she said, "we'll all have fun doing the firecrackers together."

After Mother had gone we sat on the piazza and painted our books and listened to the "pop—pop—pop, bang, boom," all around the lake. About halfway through the morning, when we were getting tired of painting, Albert rowed across the lake to visit us and brought three packs of firecrackers.

"I thought maybe you didn't have any. I didn't hear any noise over here," he said. "I brought one for each of you."

We thanked him very much and showed him our box of fireworks inside the camp and explained that we couldn't set them off till Mother and Daddy came home. Albert understood and said, "All right, I'll keep these for myself." He sat on the piazza with us and set them off, one cracker at a time, so they lasted a long while.

"We've got a big flag out, over at our house," he said proudly.

"We have a flag, too," said Beany. "Daddy will put it up when he comes."

"Let's put it up now," Albert suggested.

So we brought it out and worked a while trying to set up the pole in the ground. But it would lean sideways! "I'll tell you where the flag would look best," said Albert. "At the very top of one of the tall pines."

"That's a keen idea," said Jack. "Let's do it."

We looked around for a good pine tree. The trouble with pine trees is that they keep on growing at the tips of the branches, but the lower limbs die and break off. So the big pines all around our camp, about a hundred years old, I guess, grow up straight and tall, higher than a house before the branches begin, and there is nothing to pull yourself up by.

"I know," said Beany. "Let's climb up to the top of that easy maple that has a branch bending down. Then we can reach the lowest branches of the pine tree and swing across." He pulled himself up to the low branch of the maple and began to climb.

"You'd better be careful," said Albert. "You're too little to climb that high."

"I am not." Beany was indignant. "I always remember the rule of three."

"What you mean, the rule of three?" asked Albert.

"Daddy told it to us," explained Beany. "You have four things to hold on by when you climb a tree—two hands and two feet. And you must always keep three of them holding on, and only reach with one at a time in case a branch should break."

"That isn't the way monkeys do it," argued Albert. "I've seen them at Franklin Park and they can swing by one hand."

"They can swing by a tail," Beany retorted, looking down on Albert from the maple tree. "But we're not monkeys."

Jack was still on the ground. "This other pine tree is taller," he said. "The flag would look better there. And we can reach it—see— if we get up on the roof and then up that oak and then across on that long branch up high there. Only I can't climb and carry the flag, too."

"I'll carry the flag," I said. "I can reach it up to you and then climb up where you are."

"You can't climb a tree," said Albert. "Girls can't climb trees."

"Of course, she can," said Jack. "She can climb any tree you ever saw."

He went in for some cord and then got up on the roof by way of the piazza railing, and I reached the flag up to him, and then he gave me a hand and I got up beside him. Then he climbed the oak tree a little way and waited there till I handed him the flag and climbed up to him. Then I took the flag again, and he went up a little farther, and so we kept going till we were as high as the lowest branch of the big pine. It spread right across to our oak, and we got a foothold on it while we were still holding to the branches of our tree. After that it was easy, going up the pine. It was like climbing a ladder, while we took turns climbing and holding the flag. Only we had to be very careful about dead branches, and Jack said to me, "Don't forget the rule of three."

"Hey, look at me," shouted Beany. "See how high I am!" But I couldn't see him because the pine needles were so thick around me.

Then suddenly instead of pine needles, there was clear sunlight, with blue sky overhead, and we had reached the top and were swaying there in the wind. All around below us were layers of green branches, and beyond, far below, the blue lake and boats like toys and roofs of toy cottages on the shores. Then there was a circle of woods and, beyond that, farms and woodland like a checkerboard, and cutting through them a long white ribbon that was Route One, with little dots moving on it for cars.

Jack pulled the cord out of his pocket. I held the flagpole steady while he tied it to the very top of the tree, and the flag floated out in the breeze.

Then we came down. Jack went first because it wasn't so easy as going up, and he could tell me where to find foothold at the hard places. When we got to the ground, we stood off to see our flag. It looked very beautiful floating out straight against the wide blue sky, and I thought of America, "beautiful for spacious skies." Albert raised his hand in salute and began, "I pledge allegiance to the flag," and Jack and I joined in. We all three stood up very straight and said it all through.

We looked up and there was Beany far above us. He had climbed up to his tall pine by way of the easy maple. He had reached up to a branch too far above his head and had pulled himself up till he was doubled up over it with no foothold and was balanced there, seesawing on his stomach.

"I guess," said Albert, "Beany must have forgotten the rule of three."

"Hold tight, Beany," Jack called. "Don't let go."

Beany never answered.

"Don't let go, Beany," Jack called again. "I'm coming." He went up the maple as fast as he could climb.

"If Beany should let go!" I thought, and I felt like crying, too. I couldn't see how Jack was going to get him down. I didn't see how Beany could stretch down to get foothold unless Jack lifted him off the branch, and Jack couldn't let go of the tree to lift him without losing his own balance. I stood looking up till my neck ached, watching Jack as he went up, up, that tall pine. Once I heard a branch crack and he swung his feet quickly to another, and then the broken limb came crashing down. And then he was there, with his hands on the big branch below Beany. I watched him pull himself up till he was kneeling on the branch, holding by his hands to a stump of a limb next to it, so that his back was level like a floor under Beany's feet. I couldn't hear what he said, they were so far above us. But I saw Beany, still doubled up over the higher branch, fumbling with one foot till he found Jack's back. Then he stepped on it and straightened himself till he could get his hands on the upper branch and so let his feet down to the lower one. Jack steadied his feet for him on the lower branch, and when Beany had found his foothold, Jack swung down to the next branch. So they both came safely down again, Jack coming first, each time finding the easy way for Beany's feet.

I just hugged Beany when they got down and I would have hugged Jack even harder, but I knew he wouldn't like it with Albert there.

Just then we heard our car tooting on the mainland, and we all ran down to the wharf. Mother and Daddy were on the other side, waving to us. They got into the boat that Mother had left on the shore and Daddy started to row. Mother leaned forward and said something to him, and he stopped rowing and looked around. Then he and Mother both gazed up at the flag, floating above all the tall pines, the highest thing in sight except the clouds. Then Daddy began to row quite fast and soon they were at the wharf with all of us crowding around and Reginald barking great shouts of welcome.

Mother explained that Great-aunt Charlotte had had many people she wanted to see in her one day. So Mother had stayed for only a little chat. Then she and Daddy had hurried home so that we could set off our fireworks.

We all came up the walk together, and Mother stopped short.

"Why!" she said in surprise. "What's this?" She was looking at the litter of burnt red paper all over the grass.

"Oh, those were Albert's firecrackers," said Jack.

"He brought them to give to us," I explained.

"But we didn't fire off a single one," said Beany, "because you said not to."

"I set them all off myself," said Albert.

"I see," said Mother.

"How did the flag get up there?" Daddy asked.

"Jack tied it there," said Albert.

"But it was Albert's idea," Jack added, wanting to be generous.

"You mean Jack climbed that tall pine all by himself?" said Mother.

"Oh, no," said Jack quickly. "Dee came up, too, and helped me."

"Mercy me!" said Mother. She sounded just like Great-aunt Charlotte.

"I climbed a tree, too," broke in Beany proudly. "I climbed that one—see?—'way up to where those two big branches are. But I couldn't get down again and Jack climbed up so I could stand on his back."

"It was very brave of Jack," I told Mother, "because if Beany had upset his balance, they both would have fallen."

"There's to be no more climbing pine trees around here," said Daddy.

"Oh, but, Daddy, we've got to take the flag down," said Jack. "The colors have to be lowered at sunset."

"Well," said Mother, "we can consider that later. How about lunch?"

After lunch we set off the firecrackers. Daddy helped and Mother watched. We had a lot of fun, but before we quite finished, there was a thunderstorm. So we all went inside the camp and tossed the firecrackers out through the door as we lighted them. It blew terrifically, and in the midst of the thunder and lightning, there was a great crash on the roof. We all thought that a tree had fallen and we ran out to look. It was our flagpole, blown down by the wind, and there was our flag draped over the chimney, flapping furiously.

So we didn't have to climb the tree to lower the colors, after all, and we never have climbed the pines again. We do go up in the maple trees and the oak trees.

But sometimes when I am going to sleep and the wind is blowing, I think for a moment that I am swaying again at the top of the big pine, with the lake far below. And it seems that I can reach up my hand and touch the sky.

ELIZABETH RHODES JACKSON

# FAMOUS PEOPLE

MAGELLAN AT THE STRAIT

1520 A.

# Magellan and the First Voyage Around the World

WHEN Columbus discovered America in 1492, he was trying to sail around the world. The first man whose ship actually did sail around the world was Ferdinand Magellan.

In 1492, Magellan was a boy, living in the hills of Portugal. He knew a great deal about horses and sheep, but very little about ships and the sea. Perhaps he had never even seen the picture of a ship, because five hundred years ago no one but the King and the clergy had books.

Ferdinand watched his father's sheep. It was dull and lonely work, though there were exciting times when the wolves prowled about. His father had many horses, and Ferdinand learned to ride when he was very young. We can imagine him riding to the top of the hills, and looking far away in the hope that he might see the ocean that Columbus had sailed on. For the news of Columbus's voyage had come to Magellan's home in the hills. As he watched the sheep, the boy thought of the wonderful ships he had never seen, and of the brave men who left their homes to sail to strange lands.

When Magellan was fifteen years old, he left the hills to go to the King's palace in a city by the sea. Boys did not go to school and college in those days. Some boys became pages of the Queen. The pages had many duties: they attended the Queen when she went hunting; they carried messages for her; they served her at the table. They were taught to speak well, to ride well, and to hunt.

Magellan was a page of the Queen, and as far as we know, he did his work well. But his thoughts were still with ships and the sea. He used to go down to the shore where the sailing ships were at anchor, and watch for a chance to go on board one of them and talk to the sailors.

There were, of course, no steamships, and the sailing ships were very small. They looked large and exciting to young Magellan, though, as he stood on the tiny deck and looked up at the masts. He liked the smell of the sea. He liked the smell of the ships. They smelled of spices, cinnamon and nutmeg and ginger.

He talked with the sailors and asked them many questions. The sailors grew tired of answering him, but his dress showed he was the Queen's page, so they did not dare send him away.

He wanted to leave the King's palace and go to sea. A wise old sailor told him to wait, to study maps and learn about ships, and to get ready for the voyage he would make some day.

When he was older, he went on voyages for the King of Portugal, looking for new spice islands. He became a soldier of the King and was wounded so that he was lame the rest of his life. But when he tried to tell about his plans for his great voyage, the King would not listen. He was so unfair that Magellan left his home in Portugal and went to Spain.

Magellan told the King of Spain that he wanted money, men, and ships, so that he could sail south, then west, to the islands where the spices grew. He thought he could find a way through. Magellan did not know that way. No one knew it. It would be a voyage of discovery.

The King thought a long time, and talked it over with many people. It was hard for Magellan to be patient as the days passed and there was no word from the King. At last the good news was brought to him by the King's messenger:

"You may have five ships. You will be captain in command of all the ships."

After many days the little fleet of ships sailed out of the harbor of Seville in Spain. The ships were very small and they were not comfortable. The decks were small. There was no ice to keep food fresh in warm weather, and there were no canned vegetables and fruit. Only brave men would dare sail in these small ships to strange lands. Magellan was the leader of these men and perhaps the bravest of all.

The ships sailed south and west, as Magellan had planned. Some of the men thought him very foolish to sail west when they all knew that the spice islands were in the east. Captain Magellan, however, was sure that the earth was round, and that he would reach those islands if he sailed far enough to the west.

The weather was stormy and the sailors were discontented. One day the fog lifted, the sun shone, and Magellan's dream came true. He and his men had found the short way through the land. It was an arm of the sea, narrow like a river, but very long and very cold and dreary. It took them five weeks to sail through to the ocean. Look on the map of South America and you will see the name of this short way, the Strait of Magellan.

When they came out on the great ocean, it seemed so quiet after the wild winds in the Strait of Magellan that Magellan named it the *Pacific* or "peaceful" ocean.

They had many adventures on the Pacific Ocean, pleasant ones when they visited friendly natives on some island, frightening ones when the natives were fierce and warlike.

When they left Spain, the little ships were well stocked with biscuits, wine, beans, olive oil, cheese, raisins, sugar, onions, and figs. Before they got back to Spain, there was little food left, and men were trying to eat sawdust, boiled leather, and the rats that were on the ship. Only one ship with about twenty men returned to Spain. Magellan, the leader and planner, was killed by the natives of one of the Philippine Islands.

It is a wonderful story and a sad story. Magellan and his men made a glorious voyage of discovery that will never be forgotten. After his death, Magellan's men sailed across the Indian Ocean, around Africa into the Atlantic Ocean, and home to Spain. They showed that the earth is round, and they were the very first persons in the world to do this marvelous thing!

MILDRED BATCHELDER RICHARDS

# William Penn

WILLIAM PENN, the Quaker, was a rich man and the son of a powerful admiral. He did not go so far in his belief as some Quakers, for he wore hand-some clothing and had a fine home. But he saw that the only way for his Quaker friends to have peace was to go to live in the New World, as others who suffered for their religion had done.

To carry out his plan, he used his own large fortune. It happened that King Charles II owed Penn eighty thousand dollars. But Penn saw a way for the King to get rid of the debt, and yet not pay out a penny.

"Will you give me land instead of money?" he asked.

"Willingly," said the King.

You see, the land had cost him nothing. So he set off for Penn a large tract lying west of the Delaware River, and called it Penn-sylvania, which means "Penn's woods." Penn was so modest that he did not wish the country named for himself. So the King said, "We will name it for your father."

The next year (1681) a colony of about three thousand settled on the banks of the Delaware. In October of the year following, Penn himself left England to join his colony. Bidding good-by to his wife and children, he sailed for America in the ship *Welcome* with one hundred passengers. Most of these were Quakers who had been Penn's neighbors in England.

After a voyage of two months they landed at Newcastle, Delaware, where they were greeted with shouts of welcome. This was not his own colony, but some of those who came the year before had settled here, among the Swedes and Dutch.

Penn sailed on up the Delaware River until he came to the mouth of the Schuylkill River. Here he found a city laid out by those who had come before him. He named it Philadelphia, which means "City of Brotherly Love." This name showed the feeling which Penn had for the settlers, and wished them to have for one another.

Settlers came in such large numbers that houses could not be built fast enough. For a time some of them had to live in caves dug in the riverbanks. The first houses were built of logs, and were very simple. They had only two rooms, and no floor except the bare ground. But in less than three years many houses of boards had been put up and some had been built of the bright red brick of which Philadelphia today has so many. The city grew very rapidly, and so did the whole Quaker colony.

This was partly because the Indians were friendly. Penn had made friends of them at the start. One day he held a meeting with them under the spreading branches of a large elm tree, and together they smoked the pipe of peace.

"The friendship between you and me," said Penn, "is not like a chain, for the chain may rust; neither is it like a tree, for the falling tree may break. It is as if we were parts of one man's body. We are all one flesh and blood."

Of course these words pleased the Indians, for they had feelings very much like those of white men. They replied to Penn in words as kind as his own. Handing him a wampum belt of peace, they said, "We will live in love and peace with William Penn as long as the sun and moon shall last."

WILBUR FISK GORDY, from *Leaders in Making America*

# George Washington

VIRGINIA was once a wilderness. Wild beasts lived there, and swift Indians ran through grass and swamps. In the fall the Indians went to the shore and pitched their camps on the bluff where Pope's Creek falls into the great Potomac River. Here they fished and caught oysters, and threw the empty shells around their wigwams. The shells piled up and up, until at last the top of the bluff became an oyster-shell hill.

Then across the sea came the men from England and chased the Indians away. The Englishmen settled on the land, and their king ruled over Virginia. One of these men from England was John Washington. He chose the land around the oyster-shell hill, where he built a home for his family. He cleared much wilderness and made a big farm. And here on Wakefield Farm, more than two hundred years ago, his grandson's son, George Washington, was born.

He was born in a little red brick house that his father had built on the oyster-shell hill. By that time so much land had been cleared that the wilderness was far in the distance, hidden in the blue haze. Horses and cows had their pasture where wild beasts had lived, and black slaves worked on the Indian hunting grounds. For the hunting grounds had become great fields of grain and tobacco. George heard about the Indians from his father when they walked around together looking after the farm, which was now so big that they called it a plantation. And he learned that all the family were both fed and dressed by the crops that grew in the fields.

The tobacco leaves were sent on ships to England. There they were exchanged for beautiful clothing, like the suit he wore himself, and for other fine things they did not yet know how to make in Virginia. The humming birds shot through the air, the wild turkey clucked to her chicks, and little George dug and planted in a corner of his mother's garden. He had only himself to play with, for his sister Betty was still a baby and the children on the next plantation lived very far away. It was much too far to walk, and he was still too small to ride a pony.

But as soon as his feet could reach the stirrups his father gave him a pony, and he began to learn to ride. At first the pony jumped and shook itself. But George hung onto the mane and did not show that he was afraid. So it was not long before he could sit firmly in the saddle and hold the bridle right. Then he and the pony were friends, and he rode with his mother and father to visit the neighboring plantations.

By this time too the Washington family had left the oyster-shell hill. They were living at Mount Vernon, another plantation his father owned higher up on the great Potomac River. And George now had some little brothers to play with and look after.

In the evening his mother called the children together, and they all sat quietly around the fireplace in the living room. She told them stories from the Holy Bible, and on the shiny tiles of the fireplace there were painted pictures of the stories she told. Thus George learned his Bible, and he learned to be good and honest and never tell a lie.

When George Washington was old enough to go to school, his father decided to move from Mount Vernon to another plantation he had bought.  In a big carriage the whole family drove through deep forests.  Tall trees shut out the light, and from behind the trunks birds and beasts peered curiously at the travelers.  But George did not see any Indians, for the Indians lived still deeper in the wilderness.  Even so he had many adventures on his journey, for the roads were bad and it was difficult to travel in those days.  Every now and then the wheels stuck in a mudhole, or a rotten tree fell straight across the road.  Then the horses jumped over the tree and quite forgot that the carriage could not jump too.  But the Washingtons reached Ferry Farm, on the Rappahannock River, safely.  That was their new home.

Now George Washington was taught to read and write, and he also learned to dance.  For every boy and girl in those days had to know how to dance.

One day two young and handsomely dressed gentlemen arrived.

They were his grown-up half brothers. He had never seen them before, for they had been away to school in England. At first George was so shy that he almost stumbled over his own feet, but it was not long before he and his brothers were friends. He loved his oldest brother, Lawrence, most. Lawrence was an officer, and George wanted to be an officer too. So he played that he was general and drummer and scared all the chickens when he led his sister and brothers to great and glorious wars.

He was big enough now to saddle his pony himself in the morning and ride to school in Fredericksburg Town. He was tall and strong, and rode his horse better than any other boy of his age, and he beat them all in races and games. His friends said he was so strong that he could throw a coin across the Rappahannock River. At school he was clever too, for he was eager to learn and listened to his teacher. In his copybook he wrote down all the rules a gentleman should know. He wrote:

In the presence of others sing not to yourself nor drum with your fingers
    nor feet.
Give not your advice without being asked.
Undertake not what you cannot perform, but be careful to keep your
    promise.
Let your countenance be pleasant, but in serious matters somewhat grave.

George Washington was only eleven years old when he lost his father. Then his mother was not very rich, so he could not go to school in England as his half brothers had done. He had to learn how to provide for himself. He became serious and studious and taught himself many things. Because he was clever at arithmetic and loved outdoor life, he began to study surveying. He wanted to go into the wilderness, where only the Indians lived, and measure up the unknown land. He measured up the fields of the plantation, and till late into the evening, while the fireflies glittered over the fields, he worked with his compass and ruler and drew maps of the land he had measured.

His half brother, Lawrence, was rich, for he had inherited Mount Vernon, and he asked George to come and stay with him there for a while. Lawrence always had many elegant guests, and when George came they all liked him because he was bright and well brought up. He watched them all and learned how to bow and take snuff and converse politely. He was so tall now that he almost looked like a

grown-up man. And nobody was better than he at riding and hunting. Once, at a fox hunt at Mount Vernon, he met Lord Fairfax, the richest man in Virginia. After that Lord Fairfax always wanted him along when he went hunting. He thought so much of George that he asked him to become one of his surveyors and measure up his great lands that stretched far into the wilderness.

Together with the other surveyors George Washington set off. He worked hard and made maps of the land, and at night he slept on the bare ground. Often wind and rain tore the tent from over his head, but he did not mind, for he was strong as a bear. He rode over high hills and deep valleys and through endless forests. Far, far away from other people he came to some small farms. There lived the backwoodsmen. Their children had never seen a stranger before, and were almost as shy as rabbits. But George knew the ways of his own little brothers and soon made friends with them. Still deeper in the forest he met the trappers, who lived by catching fur-bearing animals. They had not brought their children along, for here the land of the Indians began.

One day he met a tribe of Indians coming from war with scalps at their belts. George Washington and his friends gave them presents, and the Indians danced their war dance for them. They were friendly with the surveyors, and smoked peace pipes with them. This was the first time George Washington had seen a tribe of Indians, and he thought their war dance very funny. But now the surveyors had reached the end of the Fairfax lands and were ready to return. Lord Fairfax was very much pleased with the maps George Washington had made. Other people, too, asked him to survey their land, and soon he was made surveyor for the whole county. So he traveled all over Virginia and got to know the wilderness and the ways of the Indians better than most other men.

INGRI and EDGAR PARIN D'AULAIRE, from *George Washington*

# Lafayette

THE man whom we call Lafayette and whom we admire as a great national hero was born in 1757. His full name was Marie Joseph Paul Yves Roch Gilbert le Motier. That long list of names was given to him because of the old French custom of giving to a child the names of many of his ancestors. The family called him Gilbert. Lafayette was born in a chateau at Chavaniac, a little place near the important city of Lyons in southern France.

Gilbert's father was killed in the battle of Minden when the boy was not yet two years old. Many of his ancestors had died while fighting and many were the legends of adventures that Gilbert heard. One ancestor had ridden by the side of Joan of Arc and fought against the English.

His mother spent most of her time in Paris with her father, going down once a year to Chavaniac for a short holiday. She died when Gilbert was thirteen, and he became one of the richest boys in all France. He went to school as did other sons of rich men, but what gave him the greatest delight was a commission as subofficer in a famous regiment, the Black Musketeers. Gilbert was then only fourteen.

A year later, his great-grandfather arranged a marriage for him with a very wealthy girl, of the famous Noailles family. They were married when Gilbert was seventeen and Adrienne fourteen.

The Duke of Gloucester was strongly opposed to the policies of his brother, King George III of England, especially as to the treatment of his subjects in America. The Duke told Lafayette that the war in America was all wrong; and then, according to the story that has long been believed, Lafayette determined to go to America and fight for the cause of liberty. Above everything, he had wished from his childhood to go to foreign lands and have a career of glory. Here was his chance.

It would take long to tell of the troubles which Lafayette met in carrying out his plan. His family was opposed, and so was the French government; and there were clever and envious persons who did not want him to go. But the twenty-year-old soldier had his way, and the *Victoire* sailed for America. All expenses of the voyage were paid by Lafayette. There were sixteen French officers aboard, among them Baron de Kalb. He was a very different person from Lafayette but he also became one of the most valued officers of the American army, and died a hero at the battle of Camden.

Today it takes less than a week to cross the Atlantic, but the *Victoire* spent almost eight weeks going from coast to coast. Lafayette landed in a little inlet on the South Carolina coast. He and de Kalb finally made the seventy difficult miles by land to Charleston. After ten days, he started to Philadelphia with his companions, taking four carriages, with a number of people riding horses. The 600 miles were covered in thirty-three long days.

At Philadelphia, the Continental Congress was in session. It was seen that Lafayette was different from other Frenchmen who had been asking favors. This young officer earnestly wished to fight for the American cause, and had money to spend for clothing and arms for the soldiers. At first, however, Lafayette was much disappointed by his reception. He was angry, but he could not go back to Paris to be laughed at there. On the evening of the day when he was so coldly received he sat down and wrote a letter to Congress. Here is a part of that letter:

"After the sacrifices that I have made in this cause I have the right to ask two favours at your hands; the one is to serve without pay, at my own expense; and the other that I be allowed to serve first as a volunteer."

Congress was not used to that kind of letter. To Lafayette's great

joy, he was made major general. It was not strange that
Washington was displeased
to hear that the youth of nine-
teen from France had been
made major general.

On the next day, Wash-
ington saw Lafayette at a
dinner given in honor of the
commander in chief and said
to his guest, who was surprised at the ragged appearance of the army, "We are
rather embarrassed to show
ourselves to an officer who
has just left the army of
France."

Lafayette's reply could
not have been better worded
to win the affection of his su-
perior: "I am here, Sir, to
learn and not to teach."

Lafayette's liking for Washington grew into worship, and the
French officer became one of the few persons for whom Washington
ever acquired a profound affection.

At Brandywine Creek Lafayette was wounded with a bullet in his
leg. To the surgeon Washington said, "Treat him as though he were
my son." And Lafayette continued to hold the confidence of his Commander through many trying times. In December, 1777, began the
terrible winter which the army spent at Valley Forge. Lafayette lived
in a log hut with other officers, learned to eat hoecake made of corn at

Washington's simple breakfast table, and, in general, adopted American manners.

What Lafayette did in the years of the war and what he helped France do for America is a part of history. As he deserved, he had an important position in the events leading to the surrender of Cornwallis at Yorktown in 1781. It is hard for us to think of him as a young man of only twenty-four years.

That December Lafayette sailed from Boston for France. His farewell to Washington tells much about both men:

"Adieu, my dear General. I know your heart so well that I am sure that no distance can alter your attachment to me. With the same candor I assure you that my love, my respect, my gratitude for you, are above expression; that, at the moment of leaving you, I felt more than ever the strength of those friendly ties that forever bind me to you, and that I anticipate the pleasure, the most wished-for pleasure, to be again with you, and by my zeal and services, to gratify the feelings of my respect and affection."

It might be thought that the four hard years in America would have given Lafayette enough to think about, enough glory to take back to France, and would have made him satisfied to settle down and look after his family and his lands. But that was not his way. His adventures had not even begun. Those stormy years in France had as one of their chief actors the man who became an American and was so devoted in spirit that he later took back to France enough American earth in which to be buried.

He made two later trips to America. Both were triumphs; probably no other foreigner has been so honored in our country. In all our history no other foreigner has been more loved by the American people. His memory is cherished today with that of the great Washington whom he so much admired.

WILL DAVID HOWE

## Benjamin Franklin

ABOUT sixty years after the first settlers had landed from the *Mayflower,* a man by the name of Franklin came from England. There were large families in those days and the Franklin family was no exception. Benjamin was the fifteenth in a family of seventeen children. He was born in Boston on a Sunday in January, 1706, and on the same day was carried across the street to be baptised in the Old South Church.

During his early years, Franklin gives us only one incident of his brothers and sisters:

"When I was a child of seven years old, my friends, on a holiday, filled my pockets with coppers. I went directly to a shop where they sold toys for children; and, being charmed with the sound of a whistle that I met by the way in the hands of another boy, I voluntarily offered and gave all my money for one. I then came home and went whistling all over the house, much pleased with my whistle, but disturbing all the family. My brothers and sisters and cousins, understanding the bargain I had made, told me I had given four times as much for it as it was worth; put me in mind what good things I might have bought with the rest of the money; and laughed at me so much for my folly that I cried with vexation; and the reflection gave me more chagrin than the whistle gave me pleasure."

At eight years of age, he was sent to the grammar school since his father thought he might be fitted for the service of the Church. After a year there and another year at a private school, he was taken out of school to assist his father in his business. Benjamin had failed in arithmetic, but later he took it up and mastered it, and then began on the languages. His eager young mind was on the hunt for knowledge and he found it everywhere.

His father was a tallow chandler, a maker of candles. Neither the older brother Josiah nor Benjamin liked the family trade, and both wished to find something else to do.

Young Benjamin had a great liking for the water. He learned to swim and to manage boats. Like every other Boston boy of his time, he was tempted by the sea.

Probably Franklin's father feared that he would run off to sea, and was therefore especially careful in taking him on long walks through the streets of Boston to see the joiners and bricklayers and braziers at work. In later life, Franklin often remarked that from these walks he acquired a liking and respect for good tools and an admiration for work well done by skilled workmen.

For a time it seemed best for the boy to go into the cutler's trade in charge of his cousin Samuel, but Samuel asked too high a fee and the father turned elsewhere.

He had watched how eagerly young Benjamin wanted to read, how he bought books, sold them to buy others, how he was trying to learn to write better than the models which he studied. Here must be a future printer, thought the father, and the opportunity was present because an older brother James, now twenty years old, had learned printing in London and had just returned to Boston with types and a press of his own. So Benjamin was put as apprentice to James "to learn his art and with him, after the manner of an apprentice, to serve until he should be twenty-one;" that would be for nine years.

This was a busy and fruitful time for the boy. He learned to be the best printer of his day and he read and wrote unceasingly—so well indeed that the books he wrote in his mature years would alone be a great accomplishment for any man. There were many reasons why the apprenticeship could not last the whole time. Benjamin had the best mind in Boston and certainly was the best apprentice to be found anywhere. Perhaps not unusually sensitive to his younger brother's superiority, nevertheless James was quite conscious of the fact and became more and more uncomfortable. Benjamin made his first important decision. He left after five years of service. Even in those days printers were bound in a trade sacrament so that there was no opening for the young apprentice in Boston.

At seventeen, he decided to try his chances in New York. With his friend Collins he arranged for his trip with the captain of a sloop, and sold some of his books to raise the money. New York was not so large a town as Boston; it had no newspaper and only one printer. So there was no chance in New York. However he learned that a printer was needed in Philadelphia and he set out, first across the bay to Perth Amboy and then on a walk of fifty miles to Burlington. With a companion he rowed down the Delaware River until they became afraid they would pass Philadelphia in the dark.

"We put toward the shore, got into a creek, landed near an old fence with the rails of which we made a fire, the night being cold in October, and there we remained till daylight."

At eight or nine o'clock on Sunday morning they reached Philadelphia. Here is his own story of their arrival:

"I was in my working dress. I was dirty from my journey; my pockets were stuffed out with shirts and stockings, and I knew no soul or where to look for lodging. I was fatigued with traveling, rowing, and want of rest; I was very hungry, and my whole stock of cash consisted of a Dutch dollar and about a shilling in copper.

"The latter I gave the people of the boat for my passage, who at first refused it on account of my rowing, but I insisted on their taking it. A man is sometimes more generous when he has but a little money than when he has plenty, perhaps through fear of being thought to have but little.

"Then I walked up the street, gazing about, till, near the market house, I met a boy with bread. I had made many a meal on bread, and, inquiring where he got it, I went immediately to the baker's he directed me to, in Second Street, and asked for biscuit, intending such as we had in Boston, but they, it seems, were not made in Philadelphia. Then I asked for a three-penny loaf, and was told they had none such. So not considering or knowing the difference of money, and the greater cheapness nor the names of this bread, I bade him give me three-penny worth of any sort. He gave me, accordingly, three great puffy rolls. I was surprised at the quantity, but took it, and, having no room in my pockets, walked off with a roll under each arm, and eating the other.

"Thus I went up Market Street as far as Fourth Street, passing by the door of Mr. Read, my future wife's father, when she, standing at the door saw me, and thought I made, as I certainly did, a most awkward, ridiculous appearance. Then I turned and went down Chestnut Street and part of Walnut Street, eating my roll all the way, and, coming round, found myself again at Market Street Wharf, near the boat

on which I came in, to which I went for a draft of the river water, and one of my rolls having satisfied me, I gave the other two to a woman and her child, who had come down the river in the boat with us, and were waiting to go farther.

"Thus refreshed, I walked again up the street, which by this time had many clean-dressed people in it who were all walking the same way. I joined them, and thereby was led to a great meeting-house of the Quakers near the market.

"I sat down among them, and, after looking round awhile and hearing nothing said, being drowsy through labor and want of rest the preceding night, I fell fast asleep and continued so till the meeting broke up, when one was kind enough to rouse me. This was, therefore, the first house I was in, or slept in, in Philadelphia."

At Philadelphia, Franklin found employment in a printer's shop. This was a happy time for him. He worked hard, read many books, and made an impression of industry and ability upon all he knew.

So began the career of one who by his own efforts became one of our greatest Americans—author, inventor, philosopher, and statesman.

WILL DAVID HOWE

# The Girlhood of Queen Victoria

WHEN the little Princess was nine years old, Sir Walter Scott first saw her; in his diary he tells about the meeting.

"I dined with the Duchess of Kent," he wrote, "and was introduced to the little Princess Victoria—the heir-apparent to the House, as things now stand. This little lady is educated with much care, and watched so closely that no maid has a moment to whisper, 'You are the heir of England.' I suspect we should find that some pigeon or other bird of the air had told her."

But Sir Walter Scott was wrong. Not even a little bird had carried the news to her that she might one day be Queen of England. It was not until some years later that she was told.

She was sitting in her schoolroom one day with her governess, studying her history lesson, when she turned over the page of the history book and found between the leaves a new list of the kings and queens of England which had been placed there.

"I never saw this before," she said, looking up.

"It was not thought necessary that you should, Princess," answered the governess.

There was silence, while Victoria sat motionless, studying the paper.

"I see I am nearer the throne than I thought," she went on slowly.

"So it is, ma'am," said the governess, watching her.

Again there was silence for a few minutes. Then she said, "There is much splendor, but there is much responsibility."

Then, suddenly, all the primness vanished, and the child's true character came out. This great inheritance, this load of responsibility resting so quaintly on the childish shoulders, was something very real to her.

Turning to her governess, she held out her hand and said simply, "I will be good."

Looking forward into the dim years of the future, well might she have felt the need for a hero's strength to fight for and uphold the honor of England. Instead there she stood, a little, round-faced, fair-haired child with earnest eyes and uplifted hand, but greater than any soldier's vow sounded the simple, childish words, "I will be good."

It is five o'clock on a June morning, in the year 1837. London is not yet awake. Four high officers of the state are knocking and ringing loudly at the outer gate of Kensington Palace. They have come straight from the deathbed of William IV. They have news of the highest importance for the young Princess within. At this early hour of the day the whole palace is asleep, and the knocking and ringing have to be repeated many times before the watchman is awakened. You see him rubbing his eyes and slowly opening the gate. Now the little party, which includes the Archbishop of Canterbury and the Lord High Chamberlain, enters the courtyard, and another long wait follows.

At length, the visitors are admitted to a lower room of the palace, and there they seem to be quite forgotten. They ring the bell. When it is answered, the Lord High Chamberlain asks that the attendant of the Princess Victoria be sent to tell her Royal Highness that high

BILLIE
PARKS

officials wish to speak with her on business of the utmost importance.

There is another long delay, and again the bell is rung. The attendant of the Princess appears. She declares that the Princess is in such a sweet sleep that she must not be disturbed.

"We are come on business of state to the Queen," says the Lord High Chamberlain, "and even her sleep must give way to that."

A few minutes later the door opens again. A young girl of eighteen enters the room. She has not waited to dress. Her hair falls loose upon her shoulders; she has thrown a shawl around herself, and put on her slippers. Tears are in her eyes as she learns that her uncle, the King, is dead, and that she is Queen of England!

At once she turns to the Archbishop, and says very simply, "Pray for me!"

All kneel together, and the prelate prays to the Most High to give the young sovereign an understanding heart to judge so great a people.

Adapted from J. EDWARD PARROTT

HERBERT
RUDEEN

# Hans Christian Andersen

IN AN old tale which many girls and boys love, a little duck just out of the shell looked about him and said, "How wide the world is!" And his mother replied,

"This is not all the world. The world stretches far across the garden, quite into the parson's field."

That duckling might have lived in the back yard of a little house in the town of Odense, far across the sea, in Denmark. For Odense is the town where the man who wrote "The Ugly Duckling" lived when he was a boy. That man was Hans Christian Andersen.

Some people who have read the story of that ugly duckling say, "Why, Hans himself must have been the Ugly Duckling." And perhaps Hans Christian Andersen was thinking of his own life when he wrote the story. At least many things which happened to that little duck in the story were much like things which happened in the life of the boy Hans.

Hans's father was a poor man. He made and mended shoes to earn a living. Hans's mother washed clothes for other people in order to earn money to help buy food. Since the family had so little money, Hans went to a school for the poor children of the town. He often had to wear mended clothes which did not fit him well. Other boys of the town made fun of him. So Hans played much of the time by himself.

His mother took clothes to the river bank to wash them. Hans often sat on the bank of the river while she washed. The lonely boy dreamed dreams of fairy people. It was there he dreamed some of those dreams about the fairy people which he later told in stories for other children. Perhaps that is where he saw Thumbelina sailing on a water lily.

The little boy found his father a good playmate. The poor shoe-maker told Hans many stories. He made puppets for Hans and had the little wooden figures act out the stories that he told. Hans went for long walks in the woods with his father. Maybe it was in those woods that Hans met the little fir tree about which he afterwards wrote a beautiful story.

Hans's father died when Hans was only eleven years old. After that the boy was more lonely than ever. His mother became poorer and poorer. Hans went to work in a factory to help earn a living.

His work at the factory was not hard. In fact, he worked very little. The other workmen soon found that Hans had a beautiful voice. Some of the men said, "You sing for us, Hans, and we will do your work for you." So Hans sang songs for the workmen. He knew many plays that his father had read to him. He acted scenes from those plays for the workmen, too. But Hans stayed at the factory only a few months. During those months he dreamed other dreams. He would go to the city and act upon the stage. Perhaps he would become a great actor who would be loved and honored by many people.

Hans's mother wanted him to find other work. She said, "The tailor will take you into his shop and teach you to make clothes."

But Hans was unhappy at that thought. He did not want to sit day after day on a stool and stitch seams. He begged his mother to let him go to the city of Copenhagen and find work on the stage. At last she consented. With a bundle of clothes and a few coins that he had saved, Hans set out to walk to the big city. There he spent many lonely weeks while he tried to find work on the stage.

He tried to act in plays, but the stage directors said that he was too awkward to act well. He tried to sing, but by that time his voice had changed and was no longer beautiful.

But Hans made good friends in the city. His new friends helped him to get money so that he could study at the university. By that time Hans was older than most of the students at the great school and he made few friends among the students. So again he was lonely. Once more he forgot his loneliness by dreaming dreams. And this time he wrote the stories that he had dreamed.

Do you remember the Snow Queen, the Little Match Girl, and the Toy Soldier? They are in the stories that Hans Christian Andersen wrote. He wrote many, many other tales too. He won even greater fame with his stories than he had dreamed for himself on the stage. Not only did Danish children love his stories, but children of other lands loved them, too.

Of course Andersen wrote his tales in the Danish language. But people of other lands wanted their children to read those wonderful stories, so the stories were rewritten in English, in French, in German, in Spanish, in Italian, and in other languages too.

Hans now had many friends. He dined with kings and queens. He held little princes and princesses on his knees and told them stories. The lonely boy had grown up to be a famous and much loved man—the Ugly Duckling had become a beautiful swan.

Hans Christian Andersen traveled much in other lands. Everywhere he went, he found children reading his books or listening to

his tales. Some men would have felt very important to have so much fame. But Hans Christian Andersen said,

"When I see how far my thoughts have flown, I am frightened. I wonder whether I have kept my thoughts good and pure enough for so many children to read them."

Perhaps the children of Denmark hear the most about the man who wrote the beautiful fairy tales, since he was born in their country. He was born on April 2, 1805, and every year the school children of Denmark celebrate Hans Christian Andersen's birthday.

In the town of Odense still stands the house where Hans was born. The people of Denmark have built a building beside it in which to keep the things that belonged to Andersen. The street in front of that house looks much the same as it looked when the little boy, Hans, played there.

When children visit that building, they like to look into the case in which are dolls dressed like the characters in their best loved stories. Those dolls were dressed by little girls who lived when Andersen was writing his tales. Many children like, too, the fairy figures which Hans cut from paper. Some of his paper cuttings lie in a glass case, and beside them are the scissors Hans used when he cut the fairy figures.

In the hall of that building stands a statue of Hans Christian Andersen. Other statues have been erected to his memory, but none is better than this—the statue of a teller of tales.

NELLE E. MOORE

## Abraham Lincoln

IN THE summer of 1816, the year that Indiana came into the Union, Tom Lincoln sold his possessions and, building himself a raft, put his little fortune on board and floated with it down the Rolling Fork and the Salt River to the Ohio; and on down the Ohio to the mouth of Anderson's Creek on the Indiana side. Plunging fifteen miles into the forest, he found at Little Pigeon Creek the spot where he planned to build his new home.

He walked back to the Kentucky cabin and in the late fall brought his family on the backs of two borrowed horses across the country to the banks of the Ohio. Crossing the stream, he and his boy, Abe, began on the north shore to cut a road through the densely wooded forest of walnut and hickory toward their new home. In these woods the children saw many strange wild animals. Here was the home of the deer and the wild cat, the wolf and the bear. In the fallen leaves and undergrowth crept copperheads and rattlesnakes, while in the shadow of the trees they saw more birds than the little boy and girl could count. Stately, solitary cranes waded in the shallow water of the creek; overhead were flocks of screaming green and yellow paroquets; and in the more open places occasional wild turkeys were seen.

No doubt the long ride on horseback across northern Kentucky, the first vision of the Ohio River as it swept between its scarlet and golden hillsides, and the first serious efforts with the pioneer's axe to open a way through which the horses could carry their goods to the new home, made impressions upon the memory of the little emigrant that he never wholly forgot.

Years afterward, in telling about this boyhood home, Lincoln described it as "a wild region with many bears and other wild animals still in the woods." Speaking of this seven-year-old boy who had just come into Indiana, he said: "He settled in an unbroken forest, and the clearing away of surplus wood was the great task ahead. Abraham, though very young, was large of his age, and had an axe put into his hands at once; and from that time till within his twenty-third year he was almost constantly handling that most useful instrument."

It was indeed the beginning of civilization in that part of Indiana. The nearest neighbors were some miles away, but they lent a helping hand whenever it was needed. The Lincolns were utterly poor, but no poorer probably than the rest were. And all were rich in the spirit of neighborliness that made each newcomer welcome to the frontier community and joined with him to build his cabin and protect his household from illness and want and danger of all kinds.

The prospect of beginning life again in the thick woods, in November, without any sort of shelter and with no white settlement near by, must have frightened the young mother. But she had a husband who never lost his courage and a boy and a girl whom she loved dearly; and loneliness was not a new experience to her.

It was too late to build a real house to live in during their first winter, so they had to make out of saplings what was called a half-faced camp. Three of its four sides were of poles covered as well as possible with dead leaves and brush, and the fourth side was open to the weather, except as it was protected by the bonfire that burned day and night before the opening. They had no matches; so the fire must be watched and kept alive, or the woodsman must start another by a very slow process, with flint and steel. Indiana winters are sometimes bitter —that winter the temperature fell to eleven degrees below zero. Winds sweep fiercely along the Ohio valley and the snow drifts deep on the hillsides.

We can picture the boy and girl as they lay by night on the hard earth inside their half-faced camp, with their feet toward the blazing fire, and enjoyed the dreamless sleep that their tired little bodies had earned, while Tom Lincoln, the father, listened to the howl of the storm and, hearing the cry of the wolf somewhere in the darkness, knew that he must keep up the fire or harm would come.

Without near neighbors and without the ordinary comforts, the Lincolns found life a serious affair. There was no time for play and little chance for learning, as books were lacking, too. But there were trees to be cut down; and there was underbrush to burn, a well to dig, a garden to get ready for the spring planting, and plans to make for the real log house that they would build as soon as winter was gone.

When the weather kept them within the camp and close to the fireside, the father would frighten the boy and girl with his story of how the Indians had shot their grandfather, but he would keep up their courage by pretending that there were no Indians left in the Little Pigeon country; and the children's mother would read to them out of her Bible the stories that the boy never forgot. So, because they had one another, they were happy and unafraid.

"At this place," Lincoln wrote of himself years later, "Abraham

took an early start as a hunter which was never much improved afterward. A few days before the completion of his eighth year, in the absence of his father, a flock of wild turkeys approached the new log cabin, and Abraham with a rifle gun, standing inside, shot through a crack and killed one of them. He has never since pulled a trigger on any larger game."

There was no place where clothes could be bought for the children, nor was there any money to spend on them. Abe's cap was of coonskin, the tail hanging down behind for beauty. His shoes—when he wore any—were moccasins fashioned by his mother's delicate hands out of deerskin, and his trousers were of deerskin, too. A shirt of homemade linsey-woolsey completed his outfit. Stockings he never wore until he was a grown man. Lincoln has described the slipperiness of the deerskin moccasins and trousers when he got wet; and how, with all their stretching, the deerskin trousers never quite covered his long brown legs.

Food, except fish and game, was hard to find, and without flour or meal, and without a stove, it was hard to prepare. It is not strange that the hungry boy said in his quaint way, as his father asked a blessing on the dinner of baked potatoes, "Dad, I call these mighty poor blessings."

The next year the Lincolns were able to put up a new log cabin. This was at least a safer place to live in than the half-faced camp. This cabin had neither window, nor door, nor floor. The children slept on a bed of leaves in the loft, which they reached by climbing a row of pegs driven into the wall. The bed downstairs was built by driving a forked stake into the earth, near the corner of the room, and laying a pole from this stake across to each of two walls. On these cross-poles were laid rough boards, which were made soft and comfortable by

covering them with leaves and clothing and the skins of wild animals. Such other furniture as they had, Tom Lincoln made out of the forest timber with his simple woodsman's tools.

Here, for another year, the mother suffered from the exposure for which she was so little fitted and against which she was so ill-protected. Then came a dread disease which struck down people and cattle alike. From this plague, there being no physician within thirty miles to care for her, Nancy Lincoln died. Father and son cut down a tree and out of the green timber built a rough box for her burial. In the woods near by they made her a grave and laid her to rest.

Not long before this, cousins had come from Kentucky to live near them. Some of these cousins also died of the plague, and so there were other graves to dig, and strange boxes for the boy to help fashion. The children became familiar with the mystery of death. Nancy and Abe were now eleven and nine years old, too young to know how to make the home comfortable, and too lonely to keep up the father's spirits. It seemed impossible for the disheartened man to give them proper clothing and food. The cabin continued doorless and windowless and forlorn. . . .

Things went from bad to worse, until it began to look as if the family would be scattered, as Thomas Lincoln and his brothers and sisters had been thirty years before. Then there came a change. The father realized what the home needed most, and went back alone to Kentucky. There he found Sarah Johnston, a young widow, whom he had always known, and persuaded her to marry him.

The coming of this new mother to Little Pigeon Creek was a fortunate thing for the Lincoln children, for she loved them and cared for them as tenderly as their own mother would have done. Her three children, too, brought into Abe's life the cheer of companionship that he had needed, and saved him from much of the melancholy toward which he was always strongly inclined. She was considered rich in the little Hoosier settlement. It took four horses to haul the real furniture that she brought. There were beds and chairs, and there was a fifty-dollar walnut bureau, the first the children had ever seen. This bureau was an object of such splendor that Tom Lincoln pronounced it "little less than sinful to own such a thing."

Soon the cheerless cabin was made homelike. Into the open doorway Mrs. Lincoln had them fit a door of split timber. A window was cut through the logs and frames were set in. There was no glass in the frontier country, so they fastened sheets of greased paper across the window to let the light through. Boards were split with axe and wedge and laid on the earth for flooring. The open spaces between the logs in the walls were filled with clay.

And so the cabin became a house. These were not the only changes. Between the boy and his new mother there sprang up an understanding that soon ripened into love. She believed in him and encouraged him in a way that his father never did, and she saw to it that the ambitious boy had new and better opportunities to learn, and that his father and others did not disturb him when he wanted to read. Because she found him unlike other children, she kept watch over him with special tenderness.

Fifty years later, when he had grown to manhood and had given his life for his country, she recalled to a friend the boyhood that had been intrusted to her for guidance. "Abe was a poor boy," she said, "and I can say what scarcely one woman—a mother—can say in a thousand. Abe never gave me a cross word or look, and never refused to do anything I requested him. I never gave him a cross word in all my life. His mind and mine—what little I had—seemed to run together. He was here after he was elected President. He was the best boy I ever saw, or expect to see."

Charles W. Moores,

from *The Life of Abraham Lincoln for Boys and Girls*

# Robert E. Lee

ONE day, over a hundred years ago, a boy was born into a family of Virginia. The father of the boy was "Light Horse Harry" Lee, hero of the Revolution. Robert Edward was the name given to the little boy. In the days of the Civil War, the name of Robert E. Lee was to ring out through the whole of America.

Robert grew to be kind and gentle. His father died, and his mother became ill so that she had to be taken care of. The years passed by, and the little boy grew into a youth of eighteen and went away to the Academy at West Point to become a soldier. In this way, he began the career which was to be such a famous one.

For four years, Lee studied at West Point. At the end of that time, he graduated with honor and was made an officer in the United States Engineer Corps. He returned to Virginia, his State of the blue hills and charming towns. He met beautiful Mary Custis, great-granddaughter of Martha Washington, and married her. They went to live in a fine old house on the Arlington estate just across the Potomac from the city of Washington. Then the Mexican War broke out. Robert E. Lee was called to take his part in it.

In this war Lee very soon had a chance to prove his bravery. One evening, at San Geronimo, when some of the American forces were attacking the Mexicans, a great storm swept up the road. The Mexicans ran off to find shelter while the Americans held their ground. Lee, meanwhile, had thought of a plan. Jumping on his horse, he rode like the wind through the storm back to headquarters. He found Scott, commander of the American forces.

"The Mexicans are scattered. We are going to attack San Ger-

onimo. There is a chance for you
to take Valencia, also," Lee reported
to Scott.

Scott replied, "We will attack
Valencia at daybreak."

Lee rode back through the storm
to his comrades. At daybreak, Valencia was attacked and taken in
seventeen minutes. Lee and his
party defeated the Mexicans at
San Geronimo and Lee became a
hero.

After the Mexican War, Lee was
appointed Superintendent of West
Point Academy. And then, later, he was promoted to the Second
United States Cavalry.

A dark cloud began to descend more and more threateningly over
the South and over the North. The South wished to break away
from the Union and the North would not allow that. The North
said the Union must be preserved. The South said it had a right to
leave the Union.

Now, this made great sadness in the
nation. The little candlelit New England cottages, the bright homes in old
New York, the rough cabins in the Mid-
dle West, and the white-pillared man-
sions in the South were touched
with a deep distress.

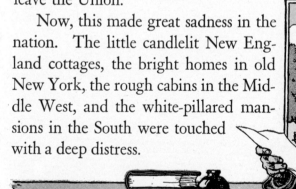

Lee felt the same sorrow that many of the soldiers of the American army were feeling. Some would join the Union army. Some would go with the Confederacy. Lee's state, Virginia, had decided to leave the Union and to go with the other southern states. Lee felt that Virginia and the men and women and children of Virginia were dearer to him than anything else in the world. Therefore he left the United States Cavalry and returned to Virginia. Immediately, he was made major general of the Army of Virginia. This army consisted of brave men from the cities of Virginia and of rough mountain boys from the hills.

Robert E. Lee became the idol of the South. He rode out on his fine gray horse, Traveler. His men gathered round him and he gave his commands with a kind seriousness that made his soldiers honor him and trust him. His hair was white now, and his bearing noble.

People thought the war would be short. But they were mistaken. It dragged on and on through four long years. The sunny fields of Virginia and Maryland were laid waste. All along the great Mississippi, the war raged. Lee's generals, "Stonewall" Jackson and Johnston, were killed. There was the heroic and cruel cavalry charge made by Pickett at Gettysburg. Sheridan and a northern army rode down through the beautiful Shenandoah Valley and destroyed and burned as they went. Sherman and a northern army marched through the South and burned southern homes as they swept by. Still, on went the war. Grant and a great northern army attacked Richmond, the capital of the Confederacy. Lee defended it with his Army of Virginia. But, finally, the North proved too strong. The South was worn out. Richmond was taken. Lee surrendered to Grant, and the war was over.

General Grant met General Lee near the Appomattox courthouse to make terms. Lee wore the jeweled sword of honor given him by the State of Virginia. All of the intense love that he felt for Virginia—its people and homes—caused him to love this sword very dearly. Grant understood this. He respected the great southern general who was standing before him, though Grant himself was the victor.

And so he did not ask Lee to give up his sword as has been the custom among nations since the beginning of history. He allowed him to keep it. Indeed, Grant proved himself to be a true hero. He told Lee that the southern soldiers might keep their horses for the spring plowing..

Lee mounted Traveler and rode quietly and sadly away to his poor worn-out army. The soldiers gathered around him, saying little but showing their devotion to him.

"I have done the best I could for you," Lee told his men. "Now that the war is over, we must try to become good citizens of our re-united country."

Returning to Virginia, Lee looked in vain for even a ghost of the old gay Virginia. Everything was changed. The great white houses stood bare. Women wore rough woolen dresses and worked in the fields. Many faithful Negroes were still about the great houses, even though they had been freed.

This was the Virginia to which Lee returned. He set himself to the work of helping Virginia and the South to build up anew. He became president of Washington College at Lexington, Virginia. Later this college was named Washington and Lee University in his honor.

Lee was now an old man, but he was still the heroic character he had always been. There was the same nobility in his bearing. There was the same kind seriousness. He was still the idol of the South. He had been defeated, but his was a noble defeat. The tall, powerfully built, white-haired Robert E. Lee has become one of America's most famous men.

REBECCA HOWE

# John Muir

TWO little Scottish boys, John and David Muir, were tucked into their beds every night by their dear mother, but in summer the darkness comes so late in Scotland that the boys would find themselves in bed while it was still broad daylight. Of course they could not sleep; so they would get up and play games. Their favorite game was one of their own invention. They called it "scootchers." It was a little like "Follow the Leader," only it always consisted of doing something daring. John, the older brother, was usually the leader.

One night John hung himself out of the window, holding to the sill with both hands. David did the same. Then John hung by one hand, and David did the same. Then John hung by one finger, and David did the same. Then John stood up on the sill and began to climb up the slate roof of the house. Slates are slippery, you know, and the roof was steep, but John managed to climb to the top, where he sat astride the roof with the wind almost blowing him off. Coming down was still harder, but he managed it somehow. Then poor David had to try. David got up all right, but coming down, he lost his nerve and began to cry.

John hung out the window and called softly to his brother, "Dinna greet, Davie, dinna greet; I'll help ye doon. If ye greet, Fayther will hear and give us baith an awfu' skelping." (Don't cry, David, don't cry; I'll help you down. If you cry, Father will hear and give us both an awful whipping.)

So David stopped crying, and John caught hold of his feet and managed to pull him into safety. That ended their "scootchers" for that night, and they never tried anything so dangerous again.

Years afterward, when John Muir had climbed many mountains, he went back to Scotland to see the house and the room from which the two little boys had made their perilous climb. Even as a man, he felt it was a dangerous adventure but excellent practice for a future mountaineer. For this was the John Muir who spent most of his manhood in our western forests and mountains.

When John Muir was eleven years old, his father decided to move to America. It did not seem safe to take Mrs. Muir and the three youngest children until there was a house built to receive them. So, to John's great delight, it was agreed that he, his brother David, and his sister Sarah should go with their father on this great adventure to the New World. Their only sorrow was parting with their dear grandfather, at whose fireside they studied their lessons every afternoon. At parting, the grandfather gave John a gold piece which played an important part in his life later on.

They crossed in a sailing vessel that took six weeks and three days for the voyage, but it was all glorious fun for the children. In America, they finally settled on a beautiful lakeside farm in Wisconsin. Fountain Lake, it was called then, but it is now called Muir Lake. After a year, the mother and younger children joined them.

On this Wisconsin farm, life was extremely hard for the boys. They worked from four in the morning until late in the evening, and there was no more school for John. Yet he managed to borrow books and so kept up with his education. Moreover, he never ceased to study and enjoy the book of nature that opened so many fascinating lessons for him every day.

While life was hard for the boys, they had fun, too. As children, they had an Indian pony, Jack, that was a great pet. The boys learned to ride at breakneck speed with neither saddle nor bridle. They guided the pony just by leaning from side to side, or by a slight pressure of the knee. They also taught themselves to swim in their beautiful lake. All this, as well as the heavy farm work, hardened their muscles and developed the strength and endurance that stood John Muir in good stead as a man.

Winter stars in the New World seemed far brighter than they had ever seemed in Scotland. Sometimes, too, the Northern Lights played brilliantly over the Muirs' Wisconsin farm. John remembered one especially fine display of them when his father had called all the family out of doors, saying, "Come! Come, Mother! Come, bairns, and see the glory of God!"

So it seemed to them all as they watched in reverent silence—a wonderful glimpse of the glory of God.

On this farm, they worked such long hours that John did not have as much time for study and experimenting as he wished. His father always had to make him go to bed. Finally, one night the old man was out of patience and he said,

"John, go to bed! Must I give you a separate order every night to get you to go to bed? If you *will* read, get up in the morning as early as you like."

From then on, John went to bed at nine in the evening and rose at one. He was inventing curious clocks and machinery, and this permission gave him time to himself. His poor father was worried about John's lack of sleep, but having given his word, he could not go back on it.

When John was twenty-two, he left the farm for good and set off for Madison. All the money he had in the world was the gold piece his grandfather had given him. His baggage consisted of two wooden clocks and a thermometer he had whittled and put together in the long nights on the farm. Yet these things he had made were given the exhibition place of honor at the Madison fair, and were awarded a prize of fifteen dollars.

In Madison, John was so thrilled by the University of Wisconsin that he made up his mind he must go there, and go there he did for four years, earning his way as he went. He earned, besides, the respect and affection of all who knew him. When he left there, it was for an active life of exploration and study in the wilderness.

John Muir might have been an inventor of useful machinery. He thought of being a doctor, but he became an authority on forests, mountains, and glaciers, because he loved best of all the storms, the beauties, and the mysteries of the great out-of-doors.

He discovered a glacier that was afterwards named for him, Muir

Glacier. He started the idea of saving great sections of our forests for national parks. He traveled in many countries and he wrote many books. His friendship was valued by writers, scientists, and even our former president, Theodore Roosevelt.

He loved children, too, and wrote some delightful letters to them, especially to his own little girls.

To Wanda Muir, he wrote, ". . . . you must mind your lessons and get in a good store of the best words of the best people . . . . then you will go through the world rich."

To another little girl he sent a description of his climb to the top of Mount Shasta, so late in the season that no one thought it could be done. He wrote, "Some places I had to creep, and some places to slide, and some places to scramble, but most places, I had to climb, climb, climb deep in the frosty snow."

That was a good description of the whole life of John Muir—our grand old man of the mountains!

MAY HILL ARBUTHNOT

# Henry Wadsworth Longfellow

A FAMOUS poet once made up a jingle to recite to his own little girl when she was cross and fretful, and since that time the rhyme has delighted thousands of children. Henry Wadsworth Longfellow was the man who composed these lines:

> There was a little girl,
> Who had a little curl,
> Right in the middle of her forehead.
> When she was good,
> She was very good indeed,
> But when she was bad, she was horrid.

Because he wrote so many poems that boys and girls love, Longfellow has been called "the children's poet."

The month of February is noted not only for the birthdays of Washington and Lincoln, but also for that of Longfellow, who was born just two years before Lincoln. As a boy Longfellow lived in a large, three-story brick house in Portland, Maine. This house was a great curiosity in Portland at that time, for all the other houses in the town were built of wood and this was the first brick house.

There were four boys and four girls in the Longfellow family, and Henry was next to the oldest. In the summer the children swam in the creek and played ball; in the winter they went coasting and ice skating.

Henry often left his brothers and sisters and went down to the wharf, where he watched the ships unload their strange cargoes. Portland had a good ocean harbor, and sailing vessels from many parts of the world came there, bringing such things as coffee and spices, silk, sugar, and molasses. Henry was fascinated by the strangely dressed sailors, although he could not understand a word they said. In later years, when he visited foreign countries, he learned some of these languages that he had heard as a small boy.

When he was three years old Henry was sent to school, and by the time he was six he could read and write, as well as do arithmetic. Before he was seven he had begun to study Latin. In the winter evenings the Longfellow children gathered around the fireplace and wrote their lessons, using slates instead of notebooks. After the books and slates were put away Mrs. Longfellow read them a story or they gathered around the piano and sang. They were slow in going to bed, for the bedrooms were not heated, and even feather beds can be very cold, especially in a New England winter.

Twice every Sunday the Longfellow children went to church with their parents, sitting very prim and straight in the uncomfortable, high-backed pews. Sunday was always a very quiet day in New England. Games of any kind were strictly forbidden, and only the Bible or other religious books could be read on that day.

In the summer Henry liked to visit his grandfather, General Wadsworth, who lived on a large farm near Hiram, Maine. He would listen for hours to his grandfather's stories of the Revolutionary War and his tales of the Indians who had lived in New England not so long before. Upon one of these visits Henry heard the story of the fight with the Indians at Lovell's Pond, which was not far from Hiram. He was so excited that when he got home he wrote a poem which he called "The Battle of Lovell's Pond." Carefully he copied the four verses and with great secrecy placed them in the letter box of the Portland newspaper, which was published twice a week. He had told one of his sisters about his poem, but no one else. When the next issue of the paper came out, Henry could scarcely wait until his father had finished reading it. You can imagine his excitement when he saw one of his own poems in print

for the first time. He was only thirteen years old, and he had never been so proud or happy before. Since he had signed only his first name, his family didn't know that it was his poem. When several other verses of his had appeared in the Portland *Gazette,* he told them his great secret.

After "The Battle of Lovell's Pond" appeared in the newspaper, Longfellow kept on writing poems. He wrote them while he was a student in college and later when he became a teacher at Harvard College. He soon became famous and his poems were translated into many languages so that people all over the world could enjoy them. Men and women from all parts of this country and from Europe went to see the author of "Hiawatha," "Evangeline," "Paul Revere's Ride," and "The Courtship of Miles Standish." When he visited in Europe he was entertained by other famous writers and even by Victoria, the great Queen of England.

One of Longfellow's best known poems is "The Children's Hour," in which he writes of his customary "pause in the day's occupations" devoted to the children. Two stanzas of this poem are given on the following page.

I hear in the chamber above me
    The patter of little feet,
The sound of a door that is opened,
    And voices soft and sweet.

From my study I see in the lamplight,
    Descending the broad hall stair,
Grave Alice, and laughing Allegra,
    And Edith with golden hair.

These three little girls were his own children. He also had two boys, Charles and Ernest. Longfellow spent a great deal of time with his children. In the winter he helped them make snowhouses in the front yard and coasted with them on the hill; in the summer he romped with them in the haymow and took them on pleasure trips.

All the children of Cambridge loved Longfellow, and many of them went to see him at his home. One little boy was greatly interested in the hundreds of books that filled the poet's library. After looking over the shelves carefully he seemed disappointed.

"Don't you have 'Jack, the Giant-Killer'?" he asked the white-haired poet.

"No, I'm afraid I haven't," answered Longfellow.

The next day the little boy handed Longfellow two pennies. "Now you can buy a 'Jack, the Giant-Killer' for your own," he explained.

On the poet's seventy-second birthday, seven hundred children of Cambridge gave him an armchair for his study. The chair had been made from the chestnut tree that Longfellow wrote about in "The Village Blacksmith." In return for this gift he wrote a poem, called "From My Arm-Chair." He gave a copy of this poem to every child that came to visit him and sit in the chair.

BERNADINE FREEMAN BAILEY

## Louisa May Alcott

ONE day there arrived in Boston the Alcott family—a young father and mother and two small daughters—one four years old, and the other, two. The family were on their way to make a home in Boston and to start a new school. It was to be called the Alcott School.

This trip to Boston from Germantown, Pennsylvania, was the first the little children had made. It was not to be the last move they would make. All the years of their childhood were to be filled with little journeys from one home to another. After a while there would be two more children. This family of father, mother, and four little girls would pack up their few belongings and, like a small company of Arabs, go traveling from one cottage to the next. This first time that the Alcott family arrived in Boston, they stayed for six years. Mr. Alcott worked hard to make his school a success. Mrs. Alcott struggled to make the family comfortable. The school was not a success, however, and so the family moved out to the quiet village of Concord.

This time Mr. Alcott decided to become a farmer. But he was very busy with his school plans, meetings, and writings, so that Mrs. Alcott and the girls had to take care of the farm most of the time.

It was not a good farm, and the family did not have much to eat, but they lived cheerily on what there was.

Two years passed. Then, one morning, Mr. Alcott said that he was going to England. There was great excitement in the home of the four little Alcotts. They helped Mother arrange for Father's trip. He left on a day in May. All summer ten-year-old Louisa was busy helping her mother sew and take care of the family. Then, one October day, Mr. Alcott returned and brought with him three friends. Louisa and her three sisters were busier than ever helping their mother in caring for all this company in the small cottage. All day long the men would work together, while the four little girls worked and played among themselves and listened to the serious conversations. Their father did not believe in their going to school. He often taught them himself at home. When the men had worked out their plans, they bought a hundred-acre piece of land near Boston and named it Fruitlands.

In June the Alcott family and a few friends moved out to Fruitlands. All summer they lived on the vegetables and fruits of this country place. Mrs. Alcott and her daughters worked hard, cooking, sewing, and taking care of the new home.

Then one day there was a terrific rain and wind storm at Fruitlands. All the men were away at a meeting. Louisa, now a girl of twelve, rushed out with her mother and sisters to save the crops which had not yet been harvested. But, in spite of their brave efforts, almost everything was lost. Fruitlands had to be given up.

The Alcott family returned to Concord and continued to be very, very poor. Their friends had to help them at times. Mrs. Alcott tried to support the family by sewing. Meanwhile, Louisa had grown into a gay, adventure-loving girl. She wished to help her family. She tried working as a companion to an old lady. Louisa did everything for this old lady—cooking, cleaning, and carrying coal. At the

end of the month she received only a few dollars. At another time, Louisa set up a little school in the barn and taught the children of the Alcotts' friends.

While Louisa was trying to earn money, she was also amusing herself and her sisters by writing plays. She and her sisters acted in these plays, causing much excitement for the children who came to see them. There were heroes and heroines and villains. There were scenes of love and hate and death. Louisa Alcott was about sixteen years old when she wrote these plays, and she began to think very seriously of becoming an actress. But this was never to be more than a dream.

As Louisa grew older, she continued to write, sometimes short stories, sometimes poetry. One day, when she was twenty-eight years old, some of her writing was published in a magazine, the *Atlantic Monthly*. All this time Louisa Alcott had tried to earn money by teaching and by sewing. To receive money for her poetry and short stories made her extremely happy.

It was at this time that the war between the States broke out. Louisa Alcott entered the Union Hospital at Georgetown as a nurse. She wrote letters home to her father and mother and sisters. These letters were published as *Hospital Sketches*. A year after these *Hospital Sketches* had been printed, she wrote a book called *Moods*. Then, the next year, she set out to visit Europe. It was an exciting adventure. But she was soon at home again, and now she was the editor of a children's magazine called *Merry's Museum*.

Friends asked Louisa Alcott why she did not write a story of all her adventures. So she sat down at her desk and began to write a book called *Little Women*. She wrote about a small cottage belonging to Mr. and Mrs. March, Meg, Jo, Beth, and Amy. And all the time she was thinking of her own father and mother and three sisters. Page after page of the gay story of four little girls, working, playing, quarreling, and loving, was written. And in the pages of this book which she was writing there appeared Laurie, the rich boy who lived next door to Meg, Jo, Beth, and Amy.

At last, the book was finished. Miss Alcott gave it to her publisher. *Little Women* was published. And then, suddenly, Louisa Alcott had enough money to take care of herself and her family. Hundreds and hundreds of copies of *Little Women* were sold. It was translated into other languages so that foreign children might read it. It has been put into moving pictures.

REBECCA HOWE

# John James Audubon

CAPTAIN JEAN AUDUBON of the French navy was living on a plantation in Santo Domingo in the West Indies when his little son, John James, was born. A few years later the Captain sailed back to France, taking John James along. The boy went to school at Nantes, but he was much more interested in the outdoors than in his studies. He loved to spend hours lying on his back with a telescope, watching a little bird high up in a tree. He drew pictures of birds and collected nests and eggs.

One day when his father was home from one of his long sea voyages, he made plans for John James to go to school in Paris to study drawing. One of his teachers was the famous painter, David. John James kept on drawing birds, and before long he had two hundred bird paintings. He was now seventeen years old. Captain Audubon had a long talk with his son and sent him to America to look after his farm in Pennsylvania.

When he had settled at Mill Grove, Pennsylvania, young Audubon continued to do the things he liked to do. He hunted, fished, practiced music, and above all, he made pictures of birds. His house looked like a museum. He strung empty eggshells on strings and hung them up. He collected stones and lichens. He pressed hundreds of specimens of wild flowers. The chimney piece was crowded with stuffed animals—raccoons, squirrels, and opossums. On his shelves were specimens of fishes, frogs, and snakes.

By this time Audubon had fully made up his mind about what

he wanted to do. He was going to make a great book filled with pictures and descriptions of all the wonderful birds of this new country of America. As long as he lived, he held fast to his plan.

Audubon had an English neighbor who had an attractive young daughter. After a while he married the daughter and ever afterward Mrs. Audubon was just as enthusiastic about birds as was her husband. Through good times and bad, through all kinds of weather, these lovers of nature and nature's creatures worked together. They left Pennsylvania and traveled for twelve days down the Ohio River on a flat-bottomed boat called an ark. They lived in Louisville for a time. Audubon built a sawmill and later he bought a steamboat. He lost all his money but he never stopped studying birds. Although the day might be bitter cold or burning hot, he went on with his work.

He made a trip to England to get more people interested in his book about birds. In England he sold paintings of American birds and other animals. He went up into Scotland and there met the famous writer, Sir Walter Scott, one of his heroes. A friend said, "Put on your coat and hat and come with me to Sir Walter Scott; he wishes to see you." Audubon was happy. He said later, "I really believe my hat and coat came to me instead of my going to them."

Audubon came back to America. He made another trip to Europe. Again he returned to his own country and studied birds from Florida to Labrador. At last his beautiful books of birds were printed. The great French painter, Girard, said,

"You are the king of bird painters. We are all children. Who would have expected such things from the woods of America?"

Today Audubon is gone, but all along the coast there are Audubon wardens, minute men who watch and protect the water birds. The Audubon Societies have havens and resting places for birds at nesting time and in many ways they protect our feathered friends.

S. EDGAR FARQUHAR

## Clara Barton

OVER a hundred years ago, near Worcester, Massachusetts, the Barton family had a wonderful Christmas present—a new baby girl. They named her Clara, and she became the pet of the household. There were two older sisters, Dorothy and Sally, and two older brothers, Stephen and David.

Clara's big brother David was fond of horses and an expert rider. He was very proud of his little sister, and he taught her to ride horseback on the prancing colts on the Barton farm. When only five years old, Clara was riding wild horses like a little cowboy. She was soon able to ride better than any of the boys in the neighborhood. She did not play with dolls, but she had many animal pets and had a flower garden of her own.

When Clara was eleven years old David had a bad fall. He was walking along on the rafters of a big new barn when a board broke. He fell through to the ground and was hurt so badly that for two years he had to stay in bed. Clara was his nurse. For these two long years she was with him constantly, leaving him only once, for half a day.

When she was thirteen years old, and after David was well again, Father gave Clara a brown colt named Billy. He had slim legs and a curly mane.  Such gallops as Clara had with Billy!  No present could have been a greater delight.

After Clara had finished going to school, she taught school for many years.  Later she went to Washington and was given a position in the Patent Office helping the government make the records of inventions.

Then came the terrible war between the States.  Many of the boys who had gone to school to Miss Barton now became soldiers.  Some who were wounded in battle were brought to Washington.  Miss Barton saw the chance to become "mother to an army and a little sister to the soldiers."  She went to the chamber of the Senate, where the wounded soldiers were brought.  She bound up their wounds and read to them.  She wrote home to Massachusetts and told about the soldier boys.  The old friends back home sent money, and jams and jellies and preserves.  The only address they used was "Clara Barton," and this was all that was needed.  Miss Barton took good care of "her soldiers."

But there were many other soldiers who needed help and care.  Miss Barton asked to be allowed to go to the front, out where the fighting was going on.  A woman had never done this before.

At the great battle of Antietam, a soldier who had been badly hurt told Miss Barton that he wanted a custard pie "all crinkly around the edges," to remind him of his mother and his home.  Miss Barton showed great thoughtfulness and understanding.  She stopped her work and made the pie.  This made the soldier very happy.

Miss Barton sometimes rode in freight cars, and often she rode horseback.  She was out there working at the front for four long years until the war was over.  She kept lists of the soldiers who were hurt or lost.  After the war she spent four more years hunting and finding missing soldiers and telling their relatives about them.

As she was now very tired, she went to Scotland for a rest.  She

traveled through France and then went to Switzerland. In Switzerland people who had heard of the fine work of Clara Barton on the battlefields in America came to see her. They told her about the twenty-two countries that belonged to the International Red Cross. They told her that the United States was the only civilized country that did not belong. The work of the Red Cross was to help in time of war to care for the wounded. When the Red Cross flag was carried, the enemy would not harm those who were engaged in this work of mercy.

Clara Barton listened eagerly to all this talk. She wanted her own country to join the Red Cross. She came back to America. She worked for the Red Cross and spent over ten years telling people about it. Some people thought that we should not join, for they said that there would never be war again. Clara Barton told these people that the Red Cross would help also when other troubles came, such as floods and fires and sickness. At last the nation believed, and the President of the United States insisted that Clara Barton be made the first president of the American Red Cross.

S. EDGAR FARQUHAR

# Buffalo Bill, Frontier Scout

WHEN Buffalo Bill was a boy the Indians still roamed the western plains. Bill's father settled in Kansas, and here the boy grew up with the Indians and the wild life of the plains all around him. He loved adventure, and liked to listen to stories about Indians and frontier scouts.

When Bill was only seven or eight years old, he was alone at home one day and was fast asleep. Suddenly a noise awakened him and he saw an Indian untying his pet pony. Little Bill reached quickly for his rifle.

"What are you doing with my horse?" he said.

The Indian replied that he wanted to exchange horses, but Bill said he didn't want to trade. The Indian paid no attention to Bill's words. The boy held his gun ready to fire, and repeated that he did not wish to exchange horses. He wanted his own pony and no other. The Indian looked at Bill and marveled at his bravery and courage. Then he quietly mounted his own horse and rode away, leaving Bill and his pony in safety.

When Buffalo Bill was a boy there were few schools. Many boys and girls never went to school and never learned to read or to write their own names. In the small town where Bill lived, he went to school in a log cabin, which was built on the bank of a creek. This little one-room cabin had in it only a few boards for desks, a stove, and a few books. Bill did not stay at school very long, for his father died when the boy was eleven years old. He made up his mind to support his mother and the other children in the family.

While he was earning money Buffalo Bill kept on having adventures. He was hired as extra boy on a wagon train that was going to Salt Lake City. On one trip, after they had traveled about thirty-five miles, the men camped for dinner. There was not a sign of Indians anywhere. Suddenly some shots rang out on the air. These were followed by whoops and yells of Indians, who had come upon the party by surprise. The men jumped to their feet and seized their guns. They fired upon the Indians, who were quickly approaching. A near-by creek with its high bank offered some protection to the white men.

"Boys, make a break for the slough yonder, and we can then have the bank for a breastwork," said one of the men.

The men decided to wade downstream back to the fort they had left early that morning. Hiding behind the bank, they slowly made their way several miles down the creek until they reached the place where it joined with the main river.

By nightfall, an occasional shot told them that the red men were still on their trail. Buffalo Bill was the youngest in the group. The day had been a hard one for him, and he was tired. Soon he began to lag behind the others. Late in the evening he noticed that he was a long distance behind the rest of the men. He was wading through the stream as quietly as possible, staying close to the bank. Suddenly he saw the head of an Indian outlined against the sky, peeping over the bank. Buffalo Bill instantly aimed his gun at the Indian's

head and fired. The report rang out sharp and loud on the night air, and with one wild whoop the Indian fell into the river. Buffalo Bill was frightened now, for he expected to see the whole force of Indians come over the bank. The men who were ahead came running back.

"Who fired that shot?" asked the man in charge.

"I did," replied Bill, who was now rather proud of himself, for this was the first Indian he had ever shot.

Bill was now known as "the youngest hero of the plains."

Buffalo Bill became a rider for the Pony Express when he was fourteen years old. He was the youngest rider on the line. This was the most dangerous work a man could undertake because of the attacks from Indians. In those days there were no railroads and the only way to carry mail to the far West was by riding horseback or driving covered wagons across the plains. Each rider had to cover fifty miles in all kinds of weather, during the day or night. Sometimes an express rider had to go over the mountains through heavy rain, or he had to make his way across the plains swarming with Indians. The greatest fear of a rider was that he might be late with the mailbags.

One day, while Buffalo Bill was a Pony Express rider, he was held up by a highwayman. Bill threw up his hands. As the highwayman reached for the moneybags, Bill spurred his pony with his foot. This made the animal rear so suddenly that one of his forefeet struck the highwayman and stunned him. Leading the highwayman's horse with its rider strapped to its back, Bill rode to the next station. For the first time Buffalo Bill was late with the mail, but he had a good reason for it.

Of course "Buffalo Bill" was only his nickname. Bill's real name was William Frederick Cody. This is how he got his nickname:

While the Kansas Pacific Railroad was being built, the company needed meat to feed their workmen. Bill Cody was asked to undertake this task. He had to supply at least twelve buffaloes a day and he was paid a very fine sum of money for this work. For a year and

HERBERT
RUDEEN

a half he supplied the company with buffalo meat. During that time, he killed more than four thousand buffaloes. From that time on, everyone called him Buffalo Bill.

One time Buffalo Bill was sent with two other men to overtake a wagon train that had gone ahead of the main group. On the way, they were suddenly attacked by a band of Indians who had been hiding in a ravine. The Indians came charging at full speed.

"How can only three of us fight so many Indians?" Buffalo Bill wondered.

But one of the men quickly jumped from his mule. In the twinkling of an eye, he shot his own animal and the other two mules. The dead bodies were jerked into the shape of a triangle and the men hid behind them for defense from the Indians.

Now they were ready to meet the enemy. The fight that followed was hard and long drawn out. Because the Indians had only bows and arrows to shoot with, they did not risk coming within range of the white men's guns. They circled around and around the small group of three, but their arrows only lodged in the dead bodies of the mules. Buffalo Bill and his comrades wondered how long they would have to fight for their lives against all those Indians. Would help never come?

Early the next morning they heard the loud, sharp reports of the teamsters' whips, which cracked like rifle shots in the air. The rear wagon train had arrived! When the Indians saw the approaching train, they made one last charge, then dashed away over the prairie and disappeared. All the men praised Buffalo Bill and his two companions for their bravery and courage. For a long time after that, people talked about the three men who had used their mules for a fort in fighting the Indians.

A very famous duel took place between Buffalo Bill and Yellow Hand, a young Cheyenne Indian chief. This was during a fierce battle with the Cheyennes, who were causing the pioneer settlers a great deal of trouble. In the midst of the fighting, Yellow Hand stepped in front of his painted warriors, his hand raised.

He called loudly to Buffalo Bill, "I know you, Pa-He-Haska (Long Hair). If you want to fight, come and fight me."

Up and down, boldly the Indian chief rode, waiting for the famous scout to accept his challenge.

Bravely, Buffalo Bill plunged forward on his horse, shouting, "Stand back, men. This will be fair play."

The two brave men rode toward each other at breakneck speed. When they were but thirty yards apart, they fired. Down went Buffalo Bill's horse, for he had stepped into a hole. Yellow Hand's pony also fell, but it had been killed by a bullet that had passed through the chief's leg. The two men jumped to their feet, and came closer. Chief Yellow Hand staggered. They were only twenty yards apart. A second time they fired, and again the young chief had missed his aim. Not so Buffalo Bill, for the Indian chief lay lifeless at his feet.

Buffalo Bill was thoroughly familiar with the country out west. He knew, better than any other, the many Indian trails, and the roads, and where to find the best watering places for the horses. He was a wonderful horseman. He was very skillful in fighting the Indians, and quick to act when in danger.

Buffalo Bill was made guide and chief scout with the army under General Sheridan. He helped General Sheridan round up bands of lawless and daring Indians who refused to obey the terms of their treaty with the government.

Although he lived a free life among wild surroundings, Buffalo Bill was always on the side of law and order, and all who knew him praised him for his honesty as well as his bravery.

IDA M. AGRUSS

# Joan of Arc

MANY years ago the English sailed over to France and fought great battles in order to conquer France for England. The French soldiers tried to protect their country. It was no use, however. No matter how bravely the French fought, the English kept winning the battles and marching on and on into the beautiful sunny land of France. They took cities and prisoners, and shouted, sang, and blew their trumpets triumphantly.

The French people became more and more afraid and more and more discouraged. The old French peasants whispered among themselves that France was lost. Some of the rich French noblemen became traitors. They joined the English and helped them instead of their own country. Besides, the French King had died and his son possessed neither courage nor a brave spirit. He did not act like a young prince who had a right to be king. He should have caught up a glorious French banner and gathered his men around him, shouting, "I am your King. Follow me and we will save France." But he did not. He sat at home in his big château, his courtiers around him, and did nothing. And so the French soldiers lost their courage.

During these dark days a young peasant girl was living quietly in a cottage among the hills of northeastern France. Her name was Joan of Arc. She was gentle and quiet and had serious eyes and

sweet ways. Everyone in the little village of Domremy, where she lived, loved her because she was so kind and gentle. Some of the time she took care of her father's white sheep up in the wild hills. Some of the time she did fine sewing or made beautiful embroidery with gold and white and blue and green threads. Often she prayed by herself in a small stone chapel where there were little stone statues of Saint Margaret and Saint Catherine and Saint Michael.

One day, as Joan was praying and the little church bells were ringing, she heard some voices speaking to her. They told her that she must save France.

Joan listened again for these voices. And soon they spoke a second time and said that she must go to a rich French nobleman, named Baudricourt. She must tell him that he was to give her a horse and men's clothes and some squires to escort her to the Dauphin, the lazy prince who sat at home in his château and did nothing. The voices continued speaking. They said that when Joan had come to the Dauphin she must persuade him to bestir himself. He must go with her against the English and save France and be crowned King at Reims.

Joan of Arc stopped praying and went home from the little church and put on some traveling clothes and started out to do what the voices had told her to do. First she went to the rich Baudricourt. When she got there, she told him that some voices had spoken to her and had told her that she was to save France. He was to give her a horse, some men's clothes, and some squires to escort her to the Dauphin, to whom she was to go immediately.

At first Baudricourt could not believe the strange words of this young girl. But Joan made him believe them because she believed them so much herself. And so this rich Baudricourt gave Joan of Arc a horse and armor and two squires to ride with her. Joan mounted her horse and rode to the château where the Dauphin lived.

The Dauphin was very much surprised when he heard from Joan about the voices. He thought, "Who is this strange girl, and why should she be able to lead my men to victory and me to be crowned at Reims?"

But Joan persuaded him to believe her and persuaded the courtiers about him to believe her. One morning, there set forth a mighty company—four thousand brave French soldiers. At their head on a white horse rode Joan of Arc, dressed in shining white armor, her hair flying in the wind, her eyes serious and sweet, a glorious white banner embroidered in gold waving before her. By her side she wore a rusty sword which the mysterious voices had ordered her to wear. Some said that it was the sword the French hero of olden times, Charles Martel, had used to drive the dark Saracens out of France. It had been found under the altar of the church of Saint Catherine in the village of Fierbois. Peasants, who had gathered to watch Joan of Arc and her company of French soldiers set out, pointed to the sword and whispered among themselves that it was a good omen.

This procession first came to the thick walls of the city of Orleans, which the English were attacking. Within the city the people were starving. Joan of Arc called to her soldiers to follow her and rode against the enemy. The starving people on the old walls of Orleans cried out that they were saved. They said that at last "the Maid," who, old fortunetellers had said, would appear some day to save

France, had come. The English soldiers were frightened. They called Joan of Arc a witch and fled in every direction. The battle was won for the French people. After that Joan of Arc was called "The Maid of Orleans."

This victory gave the French courage, and they won three more battles against the English, one after another.

Joan of Arc told the Dauphin that he must come with her to Reims so that he could be crowned King of all France. The Dauphin, this prince who possessed neither courage nor a brave spirit, did not want to go. But Joan said that he must. Finally the Dauphin said he would go.

Gathering his men around him, he set forth with trumpets blowing, flags and banners waving, and coats of mail shining in the sunlight. Joan of Arc rode in front of all this great company. All along the way cities opened their gates to them. They came at last to Reims. Clattering down the narrow streets, they dismounted at the entrance of the cathedral. Joan of Arc entered with the Dauphin. And there at last this prince was crowned Charles VII, King of France. The sun came through the blue and green and red stained windows of the huge, dim cathedral, and shone on the bowed head of the new King and the fair hair of Joan and the white banner embroidered with gold that had been carried in front of the French soldiers as they plunged into battle. And all the people watching were silent.

After the ceremony Joan approached the King. She knelt down and said that now she had done what the voices of the small stone chapel had told her to do and that she was going home. But the King said that she was not to go home. He said that he needed her to help him finish driving the English out of the country.

The King set out to march upon Paris and Joan of Arc went with him. In the midst of all the fighting around Paris, Joan was captured by the soldiers of the wicked Duke of Burgundy. This duke was a rich French nobleman who had become a traitor to France and was helping the English. He was pleased when he heard that his men had captured Joan of Arc, the Maid of Orleans. And the King, who was still without courage or a brave spirit, did not aid Joan.

Then came the great trial of Joan of Arc. The English said that Joan was a witch in disguise. The Duke of Burgundy and all the French traitors who had gone over to the English side hated Joan, the Maid who had driven the English out of Orleans and many of the other beautiful cities of France. The French traitors and the English hated Joan because she had caused the Dauphin to become King and to bestir himself to save France for the French people. At the trial it was decided that Joan must be put to death. Even then, after all she had done to help him, the King did not come to her rescue, and she was burned to death at the stake.

After the death of Joan of Arc, the English began to withdraw completely from France because there was trouble in England. The French nobles who had been traitors became loyal to France again. By the end of Charles VII's reign there was no longer any fear that the English would conquer France. Joan, the Maid, had saved France when danger threatened that beautiful land, and France was safe.

There are many statues of Joan of Arc, not only in France but in other parts of the world. On Riverside Drive, in New York City, there is a statue of her on her great horse with her sword held high as though she were still urging the French soldiers onward. In the cottages of France during the World War the peasants would hear sounds in the wind outside their cottages. And they would whisper that it was the ghost of Joan of Arc, who had returned to lead the French soldiers once again to victory and once more to save the sunny land of France.

REBECCA HOWE

# Alone: Lindbergh's Flight Across the Atlantic

BY A quarter of eight on the morning of May 20, 1927, the "Spirit of St. Louis" had been made ready. Within its enclosed cabin, Charles Lindbergh was ready, too.

"So long!" he cried to those who stood around, waiting to see the take-off.

There was mud on the field. The airplane was heavily laden. It was hard for the "Spirit of St. Louis" to lift herself from the ground, but she rose slowly, and headed for the north and east. Little by little, she gained speed. Before long, she was nothing but a gray speck in the distance.

Charles Lindbergh was off for Paris! And he was making the trip *alone!*

The Atlantic Ocean had been crossed before. But no one had ever flown from New York as far as Paris, and no one had ever crossed the Atlantic Ocean alone.

"What if he should fall asleep?" people asked.

"Sleet may gather on the wings of his plane and weigh it down," others predicted.

"He has only one engine. If that gives out, what will he do?" was asked by others.

"He may easily lose his way, and run out of gasoline," was the fear of many.

And all the time, the "Spirit of St. Louis" was pushing forward across the ocean.

There were storms. High, low, the flyer had to make his way, in order to escape the blinding fog and the heavy sleet. A part of the way, he flew as high as two miles above the water. There were times when he kept within a few feet of the tossing waves.

Once, when the sleet weighed heavily on the wings of his plane, the flyer thought of turning back. But he kept on.

"It might be as difficult behind as it is before," he decided wisely.

There were cold and dampness all along the way, although a fur-lined flying suit helped to take care of this.

The lone flyer had many miles to go, but he did not fall asleep, as some had feared he would do. Before starting the trip, he had practiced staying awake for long hours at a stretch, and had become used to it.

To help keep from losing the way, there were compasses and other instruments. Hour after hour he kept looking at these. He could finish the trip only with their help.

A steady roaring showed that the engine of the "Spirit of St. Louis" was doing its part, too.

After a night of fog, cold, sleet, and wind, morning came. The flyer knew, then, that his chances of reaching Paris were very good.

Several fishing vessels came into view. Land could not be far away, then. The flyer lowered his plane, until he was within calling distance of the vessels.

"Which way to Ireland?" he shouted to one of the fishermen.
No answer. The man only waved his arms wildly.

The lone flyer had to go on in the direction that seemed right to him. And it was right. A little farther ahead, land was seen. It was the coast of Ireland!

The flyer did not stop there. It was not his goal. He went on and on, very fast, above neat-looking farms, towns, and villages, then over the waters of the English Channel.

At last, the bright searchlight of the high tower of Paris came into view. The lights of Le Bourget were easily seen, but appeared to be very close to Paris. Lindbergh had understood that the field was farther from the city, and continued to fly northeast for a distance of four or five miles.

When he found no other field, Lindbergh returned to the one that he had seen before, and spiraled down close to the lights. Because of the many cars and the long line of hangars, he knew that he had reached Le Bourget. He had reached the end of his journey of thirty-six hundred miles. Amid shouts of a great throng of people, a perfect landing was made at the Le Bourget airport.

"Lindbergh has done it! He has made the first flight from New York to Paris! And he has made it alone!" The word had already been passed around.

"*Vive,* Lindbergh!" The people crowded so closely that there seemed to be no use in trying to get away.

Lindbergh was dragged out of the cockpit of his plane, and, for nearly half an hour, was carried around without being allowed to touch the ground.

The French military flyers saw that a rescue would have to be made. Quickly, at a given signal, they placed Lindbergh's helmet upon the head of an American correspondent.

"This is Lindbergh!" they cried.

The correspondent was really thought to be Lindbergh and was followed by a crowd to the reception committee, who had been waiting for some time.

"I am Lindbergh," the man said. Then the people followed him about. In this way the real Lindbergh was able to get away for his much-needed rest, for he had been in the air thirty-three hours and thirty-nine minutes.

The next day began a round of attending dinners, receiving medals, riding in parades, and making speeches. Kings, queens, and great people everywhere took part in the greetings that were constantly given.

As soon as he could, Charles Lindbergh returned to the United States, where the festivities began all over again.

The flyer could not be *alone* very much, for a while. Wherever he went, people followed. He had become a hero, and the whole world seemed anxious to honor him!

LAURA A. LARGE, from *Air Travelers*

# Leif Ericson

### THE STORY THAT USED TO BE SUNG

FIRST of all we shall go a-sailing with a brave Norseman whose name was Leif Ericson. He lived a long time ago—about the year 1000—and he was the son of Eric the Red, one of Greenland's bravest chieftains.

Greenland is a large snow-covered land, bound fast in the ice of the far northern sea which we call the Arctic Ocean. Only in the southern part where the sun shines longer in the summer are there little patches of green grass where people can live, and where their cows and goats and sheep can feed. It was on one of these little patches of green that Leif Ericson lived with his father and mother and sisters and brothers.

Above everything else, Eric the Red and Leif and his brothers loved the sea. They would sail anywhere in their tiny ships with the great curved prows that cut the waves. One day when Leif Ericson had grown to be almost a man, he and his friends set sail for a long journey to Norway where Leif's grandfather lived. On their way home a storm came up and the furious wind blew their ships far away in the wrong direction. Leif Ericson and his friends were brave men but they began to wonder whether they would ever see land again. Then suddenly one day the wind drove them into a tiny harbor where the sea was calm and the sand came down to the water's edge.

They did not know at all where they were, and there was no one they could ask.   They thought it was a very lovely place, so the men pulled their little boats high upon the sand and began to mend the seams and cracks which the angry waves had made.   Here they lived all summer in rough houses which they had built out of the wood that lay scattered at the edge of the forest.   Before winter came, their ships were ready for the sea again and they were able to leave the beautiful land where the wind had blown them.   They set sail for Greenland and, this time, the wind was good to them and carried them in the right direction so that they soon came within sight of home.

Everyone in Greenland was happy to see them again and gave many feasts of welcome in their honor.   Everywhere Leif Ericson went he told of the land to the south where the sands were white, where the trees grew tall and thick and where wild grapes covered the bushes. He called it Vinland the Good.   Of course, Leif's brothers and friends wanted to see this new land for themselves, and they sailed away to go exploring.   We do not know exactly where they beached their little ships on the shores of this unknown land, but we believe that it was somewhere in Nova Scotia, which lies on the ragged edge of the Sleeping Giant's cloak.

These men from the North, whom we call Norsemen, did not stay long in this new land, for the Indians were not friendly, but they never forgot it.   They told all about it in their songs.   These songs were called the Sagas of the Norsemen, and they were sung about the fires in the long winter evenings.   Mothers and fathers would sing them to their little boys and girls, and when these little boys and girls grew up they sang them to their children.   That is how the story of Leif Ericson came down to us after more than nine hundred years.   And this story-that-used-to-be-sung tells us that the Norsemen were the very first ex-plorers to discover a part of North America.

MARY LICHLITER, from *We Go Exploring*

## Davy Crockett

DAVY CROCKETT is a hero of the Southwest. His life seems strange and far away to us.

We cannot remember when Texas and Tennessee had no roads, no trains, no telephones, no schools, no automobiles, and not many houses. But that is what life was like in Davy Crockett's day.

And things that seemed natural to Crockett as a boy would seem very strange to us. Unfriendly Indians, herds of buffalo, bears, covered wagons carrying settlers and their families, flocks of wild turkeys—these were a few of the sights that young Davy Crockett saw in his everyday life.

He was born in Tennessee. He worked hard as a boy, doing the tasks that pioneer boys had to do—tasks which would seem hard work to many grown men of today.

When he was twelve years old, he was sent away from home to work—to drive a team through country that we would consider a wilderness. He traveled all the way across the country—back to the East.

In a few years he returned home again, settled down, and in time married.

Davy Crockett was a great hunter. When he was a young soldier fighting in the Indian wars, he and his company were seldom without food, because he could always hunt his own dinner in the woods.

After the Indian wars,
Crockett set out to find a new home in another part of Tennessee.   Read what he wrote about it:

"I traveled until I found the spot where I wanted to settle.   The nearest house to it was seven miles away, and the next nearest was fifteen.

"It was in a complete wilderness, full of Indians who were hunting. Game of almost every kind was plentiful.   This suited me exactly, as I was always fond of hunting."

One thing that bothered travelers in Davy Crockett's time was the rivers.   There were no bridges.   This is what Davy Crockett did when he wanted to cross a river:

"I had taken one horse with me, to pack our provisions, and when I got to the water I hobbled him out to graze, until I got back.   There was no boat to cross the river in, and it was so high that it had over-flowed all the bottoms and low country near it.

"We now took to the water and waded.   I went ahead, and carried a pole, with which I would feel along before me, to see how deep the water was.

"When I would come to a very deep place, I would take out my tomahawk and cut a small tree across it, and then go ahead again.

"We worked on till at last we got to the channel of the river, which made it about half a mile we had waded from where we had taken to the water.

"I saw a large tree that had fallen into the river from the other side, but it didn't reach across. One stood on the same bank where we were.

"I thought I could cut it down, so as to reach the other; and so at it we went with my tomahawk, cutting away till we got it down. As good luck would have it, it fell right, and made us a way that we could pass. When we got over this, it was still a sea of water as far as our eyes could reach.

"We waded on for about a mile, hardly ever seeing a single spot of land. Sometimes the water was very deep. At last we came in sight of land, which was a very pleasing thing."

How easily we drive over a bridge in an automobile, when we want to cross a river!

At one time, Crockett met the crew of a flatboat—men who were traveling up the river by "poling" their boat. He helped them pole their flatboat up the river, and got in exchange "four barrels of meal and one of salt."

The men on the boat also got off with him at the place where he was going to settle, and as he says, "we slapped up a cabin in little or no time."

After killing several deer and elk, some of which he stored in his new cabin, Davy set about preparing his new home to live in. He writes:

"We turned in and cleared a field, and planted our corn. But it was so late in the spring that we had no time to make rails, and so we put up no fences.

"There were no cattle, however, nor anything else to disturb our corn, except the wild animals, and nothing could keep them out. I planted corn enough to do me, and during that spring I killed ten bears, and many deer.

"But in all this time, we saw the face of no white person in that country, except our nearest neighbors, and a very few passengers who went by in the river boats. Indians, though, were still plenty.

"Having laid by my crop, I went home to my family, who were about a hundred and fifty miles away.

"When I got there, I had to attend a session of our Legislature. I served out my time.

"Then I returned, and took my family and what little goods I had, and moved to where I had built my cabin, and made my crop.

"I gathered my corn, and then set out for my fall's hunt. This was in the last of October, 1822. I found bear very plenty, and, indeed, all sorts of game and wild animals, except buffalo. There was none of them.

"I hunted on till Christmas, and supplied my family very well all along with wild meat (the chief food) until my powder gave out."

Here is what happened to Davy Crockett one day when he went hunting:

"I had two good dogs and an old hound which I took along. Soon my dogs started some old turkey gobblers, and I killed two of them. I shouldered them and moved on.

"At last, I came to an open prairie and saw about the biggest bear that ever was seen in America. He looked like a large black bull. My dogs were almost up with him, but they were afraid to attack him. I took my gobblers from my back and hung them up in a tree, and broke after my bear.

"In a little time I saw the bear climbing up a large black oak tree, and I crawled on till I got within about eighty yards of him. I fired at him. At this he raised one of his paws and snorted loudly.

"I loaded my gun again as quick as I could, and fired as near the same place as I could.

"At the crack of my gun the bear came tumbling down; and the moment he touched the ground, I heard one of my best dogs cry out. I took my tomahawk in my hand, and ran up within four or five steps of him, at which he let my dog go, and fixed his eyes on me.

"I got back in all sorts of a hurry, for I knew if he got hold of me, he would hug me altogether too close for comfort. I went to my gun and hastily loaded her again, and shot him the third time, which killed him for good."

And that was how you got your winter's meat in Davy Crockett's day!

CORA M. MARTIN

## Thomas Edison

### THE BOY WITH MAGIC IN HIS HEAD

MAGIC! That belongs to Fairyland, you say. Not so. It is here, in our everyday world. Wizards walk the streets of our dusty cities or dwell far from men by green lanes and grassy footpaths. And many a boy, who today is swimming in summer, skating in winter, and going to school long months every year, will grow up to do more wonderful things than any magician between the pages of any fairy book.

This is the story of such a boy. Not so very many years ago he lived in a little country village and played with the village boys and went to a little schoolhouse. He asked "Why?" about everything.

He asked his mother many questions about right and wrong. "Is it ever right to tell a lie? How can we know that God hears our prayers? Must I always do exactly as the teacher tells me? Why do we go to church and Sunday school?"

He asked his father questions about the wonderful world that we live in. "Why do we say the sun rises and sets when it does not rise and set? What makes some brooks seem to run uphill? When you strike a stone against a stone where does the spark come from?"

And so on and so on from the time he got up in the morning until he went to bed at night. Of course, asking questions is one way—and a very good way—of learning about the things around us and about the way to live. His mother knew this. His father knew it. But—perhaps because they could not always give the right answer—sometimes they got tired of answering questions. There were so many of them.

The boy's teacher became so impatient that finally he said, "This boy is a dunce!"

The boy's mother said, "My son is not a dunce. I will teach him at home, and you will see that he can learn as well as any other boy."

So she taught him at home. She was gentle and patient and he did learn. He began to be interested in chemicals which could answer some of his "whys." So his mother let him gather together all the bottles he could find and put in them such chemicals as he had money to buy. These bottles he kept in neat rows on shelves in the cellar, and

he spent many a happy hour making experiments. The magic in his head was working just as it had been working when he kept asking, "Why?"

The magic didn't keep him out of danger. Perhaps sometimes it pushed him in. Once when he was very small, he lay flat on his stomach and leaned far out over the bank of the canal that ran in front of his home. He wanted to watch the queer, wriggly things that lived in the bottom of the canal. Farther and farther over he leaned until at last in he went, ker-flop! If some one had not been at hand to pull him out that would have been the end of him and his magic.

Another time he tried to build a fire with which to make some experiments. But the fire didn't stay in the corner of the barn where he built it. It grew and grew. Men put it out, and the boy's magic did not save him from being whipped in the public square as an example to other boys.

Neither did it save him from making mistakes. One day he reasoned, "Seidlitz powders fizz. If a boy took a lot of seidlitz powders they would fizz so inside of him that he would be lighter than air. Then he could fly."

He explained this to the boy who worked for his father and the boy said, "Let *me* try. I'd like to fly."

The boy with the magic wanted to try it himself, but he was always kind and generous, so he said, "All right. Go ahead!"

The big boy took the powders. But when they began to fizz, instead of flying, he lay down on the ground and squirmed with pain.

When the boy was twelve years old he begged to be allowed to make some money for himself so that he could buy more chemicals. Making experiments costs a great deal of money, and his father could not give him so much. At last he was allowed to sell newspapers on a train.

More than that, he was allowed to keep his bottles in a corner of one of the cars, so that he could work during his spare moments on the train just as he had worked in the cellar at home. But one day the train gave a sudden jerk, and a stick of phosphorus fell on the floor. The same jerk sent the boy sprawling, and before he could pick himself up the floor was burning. The conductor put out the fire. Then, beside himself with anger, he gave the boy a sound boxing on his ears. This fit of anger had dreadful consequences, for ever after the boy was hard of hearing.

That was the end of his selling papers and making experiments on a train. But he found it hard to keep away from the railroad. One day as he stood at the little station watching the express coming swiftly toward him, suddenly his heart seemed to stop beating. For there on the track before him toddled the stationmaster's baby boy. The next instant the boy with magic jumped. Another jump back to the platform and the baby was safe, though a tap on the heel by one of the swiftly rolling wheels told the boy that only by a fraction of a second had they both escaped death.

"Never, never, can I repay you," gasped the stationmaster. "My son's life is more precious to me than anything else in the world. What can I do for you? Whatever I can do, I will do."

The boy thought a moment. "Will you teach me telegraphy?" he asked.

Telegraphy proved to be a wand for that magic in his head. At that time only one message at a time could be sent on a wire. He worked on his magic until he could send two at one time. Then four. Nor did he stop until six messages could be sent flying over one wire at the same time. And today, wherever men use the telephone or the telegraph, wherever electric light is used, wherever the voice of the radio is heard, wherever men listen to music played by hands long still, the name of Thomas Alva Edison is revered.

MABEL ANSLEY MURPHY

# Boyhood Stories of Great Musicians

### JOHANN SEBASTIAN BACH

JOHANN BACH lived with his older brother Christoph, for his mother and father had died when he was very young. It was natural for him to love music, for everybody in the Bach family for many, many years had been a musician. The Bachs were the most famous family of musicians in all Germany.

Christoph taught little Johann how to play the piano. Soon he could play all his pieces from memory. He begged Christoph for more difficult music, but the older brother refused. Christoph had one book of pieces that Johann was especially anxious to play. This book contained the most beautiful music he had ever heard. But Christoph kept the book put away in a tall cabinet and guarded it carefully. Johann had set his heart on playing this music, and he finally thought of a plan for getting it. Late at night, when everyone was asleep, he climbed up on a chair and took the precious book from the cabinet. Then he began to copy the music, note by note and page by page. It was very slow work, and he could only copy on moonlight nights, when the light shone brightly through the window. He did not dare light a candle. For six months Johann

worked at his copying. Then one night, when he had almost finished his task, Christoph found him. The boy's heart was almost broken when his brother took away the precious book and tore up Johann's own copy.

But even this great disappointment could not lessen his love for music. Sometimes he walked fifty miles just to hear a musician play.

Johann Sebastian Bach became the most famous musician of his family. He has been called the father of modern music, because he influenced all the composers who have lived since his day.

### WOLFGANG MOZART

When his sister Nannerl had her first music lesson, little Wolfgang Mozart begged his father to teach him, too. He was only three years old, and his father laughed at the idea of giving him piano lessons. But Wolfgang stood right beside the piano while Nannerl had her lesson, and then he played correctly every one of her exercises. After that Wolfgang had music lessons, too.

This child was so wonderful that people all over Austria heard about him. The Empress invited him to come and play before the court. He was at that time six years old. His feet could hardly reach down to the pedals, but he played music that was very difficult for even a grown person. The lords and ladies of the court clapped and clapped. Little Wolfgang climbed into the Empress' lap, flung his arms around her neck, and kissed her. The people all around were horrified, but the Empress was delighted.

They had the child play again and again. After he had finished a very difficult piece, one of the lords said,

"Play the same thing with one finger."

Of course no one thought he could do it. Without a word Wolfgang went through it perfectly, using only one finger of each hand. Everyone was now anxious to have him do tricks.

"Cover the keys with a piece of cloth and play through it," another of the lords suggested.

Again the child performed what seemed to be a miracle.

While he was a small boy, Wolfgang composed many pieces of his own. When his father first saw these pieces he said,

"Yes, Wolfgang, your notes make melody, but no one can play such music. It is too difficult."

"It goes like this, Father," replied the boy, as he ran to the piano and played the composition.

Throughout his life Wolfgang Mozart wrote music—in all more than six hundred pieces. Many of them are played today. They show the same gayety and sweetness that made Wolfgang so dearly loved when he was a child.

### FREDERIC CHOPIN

Little Frederic, or "Fritzchen," as his mother called him, liked to go to the river in the winter and watch the people skate. They always sang while they skated and it was the singing that he especially liked. His mother had forbidden him to go alone, because he might get hurt in crossing the streets. But one day he went anyway. His father said that if he ran away again a policeman would come after him and put him in jail.

A little later a fine carriage drove up, and a man with a crimson-plumed bonnet came up to the door. Fritzchen was very frightened. This was surely the chief of police coming to arrest him. Before he could hide himself he heard the stranger ask if Frederic Chopin lived in this house.

"Oh, Mother," he sobbed, "please don't let him take me. I won't run away again."

"What is the matter, my Fritzchen?" asked his mother. "This man won't hurt you. He wants you to play at a great concert."

The finely dressed stranger was a famous poet, who had heard that little Frederic could play the piano very beautifully, although he

was only nine years old.  The boy had never played at a public concert before, and he was excited and happy.  His mother made him
a handsome new suit of blue velvet, with
a large collar of rich lace.  Fritzchen
seemed more interested in his new clothes
than in the concert itself.

He looked very tiny on the huge
platform of the concert hall, for he was
small for his age.  But there seemed to
be magic in his fingers, and the people
applauded loudly.  They would hardly
let him stop playing.  When he came
home his mother asked him all about the
concert.  Were many people there?  Did
he have a good time?  Did he remember his music?  Which piece
did the audience like best?

"Oh, Mother," said Frederic, "I think they liked my collar best,
for everyone looked at it."

### GEORG FRIEDRICH HANDEL

Georg Handel loved music so much that his father was afraid
the boy would become a musician, and he did everything possible
to keep music away from the child.  He wouldn't let him go
to a public school because music was taught there.  He wouldn't
let him play with boys in whose homes he might hear music.  The
child wasn't even allowed to have musical toys.  But Georg liked
music better than anything else in the world.  Although he had no
one to teach him, he learned to play the piano before he was seven
years old.

Someone who knew how Georg loved music—probably his mother
or his nurse—had secretly carried into the house a little spinet, which

is like a very small piano. It was put in the attic, where the boy's father would not see it. Then late at night, when everyone was asleep, the little boy stole upstairs. Softly he picked out tunes on the spinet, and taught himself how to play.

One day when his father was going to visit one of his other sons, Georg begged to go too. His father said, "No." But the boy ran along behind the coach and the father finally allowed him to go. This older brother was in the service of the Duke, on whose estate there was a chapel. Every day Georg went to the chapel to hear the organ.

One afternoon, after all the others had gone, he climbed up on the organ bench. He played the organ just as easily as he played the spinet, without a lesson from anyone. Every afternoon he played the organ in the chapel and soon the Duke heard about it, and so did Georg's father. The father was very angry and wanted to punish the boy. But the Duke felt that Georg was a real musician and told the father that the boy should be allowed to study music. Because it was the powerful Duke who said this, the father consented, and Georg Friedrich Handel no longer had to hide his spinet in the attic.


### FRANZ SCHUBERT

Franz Schubert's father was very poor, so Franz was sent to the church school in Vienna. Here he sang in the church choir and was given his schooling, as well as his board and room, free of charge. He was not happy because his room was so cold and he did not often get enough to eat. His chief pride was the gold-laced uniform and fine three-cornered hat which he wore when he sang in the choir.

After Franz had been at the school for three years, his voice changed and he could no longer sing in the choir. He had to find some way to earn a living.

One Sunday he walked to one of the little villages near Vienna. He stopped at an inn for dinner, and there he found a gaily dressed bridal party. Instead of singing and dancing, they were all sitting around looking gloomy and unhappy. There was only one band in the village, and it was playing at another party.

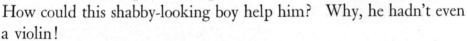

"Let me help you out," said young Franz. The innkeeper looked puzzled. How could this shabby-looking boy help him? Why, he hadn't even a violin!

The bridal party watched with interest as Franz sat down at the piano. Soon the room was filled with gay, lively music that none of them had ever heard before. Everyone began to dance. The boy's tunes had a sort of magic that made the little inn seem like a gorgeous ballroom. The music that Franz Schubert composed for this village wedding party is played even today, for these dances are among his loveliest compositions.

### GIUSEPPE VERDI

Giuseppe Verdi was born in a small town in Italy, where his father kept an inn. The name "Giuseppe" is the Italian word for "Joseph."

In those days it was the custom for men who played the violin to travel from place to place, to stop at all the inns, and to play for the guests. Little Giuseppe would listen for hours without moving. One violinist saw this quiet boy who left his play to listen to music.

He told Giuseppe's father that the boy might become a musician.

When he was about seven years old, Giuseppe was asked to assist as altar boy on one of the church holidays. This was the first time in his life that he had heard an organ. As the deep, beautiful tones poured forth, the boy stood as if in some magic spell. He forgot the church service. He paid no attention to his duties as altar boy.

At that moment there was only one thing in the world for him —the beauty of the music. When the priest asked for the holy water, Giuseppe paid no attention. The priest asked a second time, and then a third. Still the boy stood like one in a dream. By this time the priest became angry and slapped the boy. The child fainted and fell down the steps of the altar.

Soon he began to cry, and there seemed to be no way to stop him. His mother and father became worried. They were afraid that he was badly hurt. Finally he told them that he wasn't hurt, but he was afraid of what the other boys would think of him because he had fainted. In order to quiet Giuseppe, his father offered to do anything the boy wanted. The crying stopped at once. "Let me study music," said the boy.

So the father consented and Giuseppe Verdi had his first music lessons. Today the songs from his operas are sung all over Italy and in many other parts of the world.

### EDWARD MACDOWELL

If you had known Edward MacDowell when he was a young boy, you would never have thought that he would become a great composer. He lived in New York City, and he was just like the other boys in the neighborhood. He began taking music lessons when he was eight years old, but his mother had a hard time to make him practice. He wanted to spend all his time drawing pictures, and at school he covered his books and notebooks with sketches. When he was supposed to practice his music lesson he often closed the book and drew pictures on the outside of it. His drawings were really good, and he might have become an artist if he had wanted to, instead of a musician.

One day he was very much interested in a new storybook when his mother reminded him that it was time to practice his music. But he simply *couldn't* leave his book. So he hired his brother Walter to practice for him. Edward promised Walter two pennies if he would play the piano for an hour. Walter agreed, and Edward went on with his story. While he was in the midst of his book, a lady came to call on Mrs. MacDowell. Edward's mother came into the parlor and saw what was going on. As a punishment Edward had to practice an extra hour—and he lost his two pennies besides.

Although he didn't like to practice scales and exercises, Edward did like to make up tunes of his own. He often spent most of his practice hour in playing these pieces he had composed. His music teacher soon found that the tunes Edward made up were just as lovely as the compositions he had been given to practice.

When he was fifteen years old, Edward was sent to Paris to study.

Throughout his life he wrote beautiful melodies, often introducing into them bits of American and Indian folk music. He became one of America's best-loved composers.

Bernadine Freeman Bailey

# Little Stories of Great Artists

### GIOTTO, THE SHEPHERD BOY WHO BECAME AN ARTIST

TO A grassy hillside just outside a little village in Italy, not far from the city of Florence, a shepherd boy came every day to watch his father's sheep. He loved the trees, the flowers, and the birds, and he often tried to draw them on the rocks or on the ground. One day he found a smooth, flat rock. Breaking off a sharp piece to use as a pencil, he began to draw a picture of one of the sheep. A man passing by stopped to watch him. "Have you ever studied drawing?" he asked.

"No," replied Giotto, "I only try to draw things as I see them."

"If you can do so much without training and with such rude tools, I should like to see what you can do with training and with pencil, brush, and canvas," said the man. Then he told Giotto that he was Cimabue (the greatest painter of the day), and offered to take Giotto to Florence to teach him.

Before long, the pupil could do even better work than the teacher. He painted holy pictures for the churches; he painted Saint Francis feeding the birds. He made his pictures more lifelike than those of the painters before him.

Besides painting pictures Giotto designed and partly built a beautiful bell tower that is still standing in the city of Florence. It is built of marble and covered with many fine carvings. One of the pictures carved there is that of a shepherd—thought to be Giotto himself—and a dog, probably the very dog that helped Giotto watch the sheep on the hillside.

### LEONARDO DA VINCI, MASTER OF MANY ARTS

When Leonardo da Vinci was a boy, he was interested in so many things that it was hard to tell what he was going to be when he grew up. At school he was somewhat of a problem to his teachers. Sometimes he did not want to work at the tasks set before him. He was forever asking questions, and often they were questions that his masters could not answer.

He was interested in all living things, and in machinery, too. He often went into the market place and bought birds. Then he would set them free and watch them fly away.

One day he said, "I have an idea for a machine with which men could fly, too."

That was about five hundred years before the airplane was invented, and people thought that Leonardo's idea was just a wild dream. But they did use his ideas for building bridges and canals, and for some kinds of machines.

Leonardo was most interested in drawing and painting. He has left us only a few pictures, but they are among the greatest in the world. He painted the portrait of a woman, "Mona Lisa," who seems to smile right through the canvas, and people have been asking, ever since, "What is she smiling about?"

On the walls of a monastery in Milan Leonardo painted "The Last Supper," a picture of Christ and His disciples. Though the paint has peeled and faded, it is still a marvel of spiritual beauty, and people come from all over the world and stand watching the faces of the Master and these twelve men.

### MICHELANGELO, PAINTER AND SCULPTOR OF GIANT FIGURES

Michelangelo began life with the sound of stonecutting in his ears, for his nurse was the wife of a stonecutter. His greatest desire as a boy and as a man was to carve beautiful statues out of stone and marble.

He studied drawing as a youth, and did better than any of the other boys who studied with him—better even than his teacher. When he was fourteen, he was able to correct one of his teacher's pictures. Much as he liked drawing, he always thought he would rather model or carve. How happy he was when he was given his first block of marble to do with as he wished!

When Michelangelo was still quite young, he was asked what he could do with a large block of marble that stood near the cathedral in Florence. Another sculptor had tried to carve a giant out of it and had failed. Out of the misshapen block Michelangelo made a beautiful statue of young David, ready to fling the stone at the giant Goliath.

One day Pope Julius II asked Michelangelo to paint the ceiling of the Sistine Chapel in Rome.

Michelangelo said, "I am a sculptor rather than a painter. Let the painter Raphael do it."

But the Pope insisted. Lying on his back on a scaffold much of the time, Michelangelo worked day after day for four years, covering the ceiling with wonderful paintings. Great figures, which stand out magnificently as though they were sculptured, tell the Bible story of the creation of the world.

### RAPHAEL, THE DIVINE PAINTER

Giovanni Sanzio was decorating the walls of a church with holy pictures. And as he painted the heads of angels, he was thinking of his little son at home. He had given this son the name of an angel— Raphael—and the child looked like an angel with his large, thoughtful brown eyes and golden brown hair. Then an idea came to Sanzio. Seizing his brush, he painted the portrait of his son Raphael among the angel faces.

When Raphael was a little older, he loved to go with his father and watch him work, and before long he wanted to paint, too. The father gave the boy his first lessons, but died before he could teach him very much. Young Raphael was only eleven years old at that time.

When the boy was fifteen, his uncle decided that he should study with some great artist, and went to Perugino, one of the best masters. Showing him some of the boy's drawings, the uncle asked the artist whether he would take Raphael as a pupil.

"Yes," said Perugino, as he looked at the drawings. "Let him be my pupil; he will soon be my master."

Perugino's words came true. Raphael did become a great master. But he never stopped learning. When he went to Florence and Rome and saw the magnificent work of such masters as Leonardo da Vinci and Michelangelo, he saw how he could make his own painting better.

Raphael was as good and kind as he was skillful, and he seemed to put some of the goodness of his own heart into his pictures. He loved most of all to paint pictures of the Madonna—Mary, the mother of Jesus—with the Christ Child. In one of these pictures the Madonna seems to be floating down from heaven on the clouds, and the clouds are full of little angel faces. No wonder the artist who painted this is called the "divine Raphael."

## MILLET, PEASANT AND PAINTER

Jean François Millet was the son of a peasant in France. The family was very poor and both the father and the mother went every day to work in the fields. Little François was left in the care of his grandmother. After his parents had gone in the morning the grandmother would call,

"Up, my little François. If you only knew what a long time the birds have been singing the glory of God!"

She took the little boy on her knee and told him stories from the Bible. Sometimes she took down the big family Bible, which had many pictures in it, and read to him. François looked at the pictures and thought how he would like to make pictures, too. He began to draw—on bits of paper, on the walls of the little cottage, sometimes even on his wooden shoes.

Soon François, too, had to go to work in the fields. He did his share of the sowing and plowing and of all the other hard tasks. But at noon, when the others sat under the trees resting, he made sketches. His father watched him. He, too, had wanted to be an artist. One day François showed him a picture he had drawn with charcoal. It showed an old man bent down with hard work. His father looked at it and said,

"I know, my son, what you would like to do. You would like to become a painter. That is what I, too, once wished to be. I have wanted for a long time to send you away to study, but I could not. You are the eldest of my boys, and I needed you too much. But now your brothers are growing up, and I will not keep you from learning what you wish to know."

The peasant boy went to Cherbourg and later to Paris to study. He was poor, and he remained poor all of his life. But he learned how to draw and paint. He painted peasants as he had seen them working in the fields—sowing the grain, mowing hay, taking care of the sheep or the hens, gleaning the bits of grain left in the field, stopping work to say a prayer. He became a great painter, but he was still a simple peasant, who loved and understood the people from whom he had come.

### WHISTLER AND HIS MOTHER

When James Whistler was a boy he lived for some years in Russia. His father, Major Whistler, had been asked by the Russian Emperor to help in the building of a great railroad.

James, or "Jemmie," as his mother called him, was the older of two sons. He was a mischievous boy and sometimes did things he should not have done, but he loved his mother very much. On his tenth birthday he copied out a poem and put it under his mother's plate at the breakfast table. The poem was full of rather big words, but what it meant was that no matter how far he traveled he would always come back to his mother, and no matter how many friends he had or how famous he became he would always love his mother more than anything or anyone else in the world.

James's mother soon had great need for all the love he could give her, for Major Whistler died, and she was left alone with her two little boys. She sailed back to America.

James had been away from his own country so long that he seemed like a foreigner. He was different from the other boys and they sometimes laughed at him. But James could laugh at other people, too. In fact, ridiculing other people was one of his worst faults.

He had a teacher named Dr. Park, who was very tall and thin, with a long neck and a collar so high and stiff that he couldn't turn his head. One day he saw that all the boys in his room were shaking with laughter. Going softly behind them to see what was the matter, he found James Whistler just putting the finishing touches to a drawing. It was a picture of the schoolmaster. The picture was so characteristic, though of course an exaggeration, that Dr. Park himself couldn't help laughing. But just the same James received a few raps of the ruler in punishment.

Whistler never got over the habit of making fun of people, and because of this there were many who disliked him. But all through his life he kept his great love for his mother. Most of his life he spent away from America. He studied in France and lived a long time in England. Whenever he could, he had his mother live with him.

When his mother was an old lady he painted her portrait—a frail little woman sitting quietly with her hands folded. He thought people who saw it would consider it "just a picture." But almost everybody who looked at it seemed to feel some of the love this son had for his mother, and the great love and care she had given to him.

PAULINE ROSENBERG

# Noah and the Great Flood

WHEN God saw that men were growing more and more wicked in the world and that their thoughts were always evil, He was greatly grieved and regretted that He had made man. And therefore God said, "I will destroy man and all living beings from the face of the earth, for it repenteth me that I have made them."

But Noah had won God's favor, for he was a just and good man, so God said to him, "The earth is filled with wickedness and I will destroy all living things. Make thee an ark of gopher wood. Rooms shalt thou make in the ark and cover it within and without with pitch. And this is how thou shalt build it: The length of the ark shall be three hundred cubits, the breadth of it fifty cubits, and the height of it thirty cubits. A window and a door shalt thou set in it, and with lower, second, and third stories shalt thou make it. For, behold, I shall bring a flood of waters upon the earth to destroy every living creature wherein is the breath of life. Every creature that is on the earth shall die."

And the Lord said to Noah, "Thou shalt come into the ark, thou, and thy sons, and thy wife, and thy sons' wives with thee. And of every living thing of all flesh, two of every sort shalt thou bring into the ark; they shall be male and female. Of fowls after their kind, and of cattle after their kind, of every creeping thing of the earth after his kind, two of every sort, to keep them alive. And take thou food for thee and for them. After seven days I will cause it to rain upon the earth for forty days and forty nights, and I will destroy every living thing that I have made."

And Noah did all that God commanded him. When the waters of the flood came upon the earth, he, his sons, his wife, and his sons' wives entered into the ark. And of every beast and every living thing upon the earth there went in two, the male and the female, as God had commanded Noah.

The rain fell upon the earth forty days and forty nights. And the waters rose higher and higher and raised up the ark, and it was lifted up above the earth. All the high hills were covered, and all living creatures were destroyed. Noah alone was left, and they that were with him in the ark. And the waters flooded the earth for a hundred and fifty days.

Then God remembered Noah and all that were with him in the ark. And God made a wind to blow over the earth. The rain from heaven ceased, and the waters withdrew more and more from the land. And the ark rested upon Mount Ararat.

After forty days more Noah opened the window of the ark, and sent forth a raven, and it kept going to and fro until the waters were dried up from off the earth. Also he sent forth a dove to see if the waters had gone from the surface of the earth. But the dove found no rest for the sole of her foot, and so returned to him in the ark, for the waters covered the whole earth. Then Noah reached out his hand and took her and brought her back into the ark.

Then he waited seven days more and again sent forth the dove from the ark. And the dove came in to him in the evening and in her mouth was a freshly plucked olive leaf. So Noah knew that the waters had gone from the earth. And he waited seven days more and again sent out the dove, but she returned not again unto him.

Noah took off the covering of the ark and looked and saw that the ground was dry. Then Noah went forth, and his sons, and his wife, and his sons' wives with him; and every beast, every fowl, and every creeping thing that was with him went forth out of the ark.

# The Story of Ruth

NOW it came to pass in the days when the Judges ruled, that there was a famine in the land of Judah. And a certain man, Elimelech, of the town of Bethlehem in Judah, went to live in the country of Moab, he and his wife, Naomi, and his two sons. And they continued there. But the man died and his wife was left, and her two sons.

Then the sons took them wives of the women of Moab; the name of the one was Orpah, and the name of the other Ruth; and they dwelled there about ten years. And the two sons died also; and Naomi was left without son or husband.

Then she arose with her daughters-in-law that she might return from the country of Moab, for she had heard in the country of Moab how that the Lord had visited his people in giving them bread.

Wherefore she went forth out of the place where she was, and her two daughters-in-law with her, and they went on the way to return unto the land of Judah.

And Naomi said unto her two daughters-in-law, "Go, return each to her mother's house. The Lord deal kindly with you, as ye have dealt with the dead, and with me. The Lord grant that ye may find rest, each of you in the house of her husband."

Then she kissed them and they lifted up their voice and wept, and said unto her, "Surely we will return with thee unto thy people."

And Naomi said, "Turn again, my daughters. Have I any more sons that may be your husbands? Nay, for it grieveth me much for your sakes that the hand of the Lord is gone out against me."

And they lifted up their voice, and wept again. And Orpah kissed her mother-in-law, but Ruth clave unto her.

And Ruth said, "Entreat me not to leave thee, or to return from following after thee: for whither thou goest, I will go; and where thou lodgest, I will lodge: thy people shall be my people, and thy God my God. Where thou diest, will I die, and there will I be buried. The Lord do so unto me, and more also, if aught but death part thee and me."

When Naomi saw that Ruth was steadfastly minded to go with her, then she left off speaking unto her.

So they two went on, and they came to Bethlehem at the beginning of the barley harvest.

Now Naomi had a kinsman of her husband's, a mighty man of wealth, and his name was Boaz.

And Ruth, the Moabitess, said unto Naomi, "Let me now go into the field, and glean ears of corn after him in whose sight I shall find grace." And Naomi said, "Go, my daughter."

And Ruth went, and came, and gleaned in the field after the reapers; and by chance she came to a part of the field belonging to Boaz.

And, behold, Boaz came from Bethlehem, and said unto the reapers, "The Lord be with you." And they answered him, "The Lord bless thee."

Then said Boaz unto his servant that was set over the reapers, "Whose damsel is this?"

And the servant that was set over the reapers answered and said, "It is the Moabitish damsel that came back with Naomi out of the country of Moab. And she said, 'I pray you, let me glean and gather after the reapers, among the sheaves.' So she came, and hath continued even from the morning until now."

Then said Boaz unto Ruth, "Hearest thou not, my daughter? Go not to glean in another field, neither go from hence, but abide here fast by my maidens. Have I not charged the young men that they shall not touch thee? And when thou art athirst, go unto the vessels, and drink of that which the young men have drawn."

Then she fell on her face and bowed herself to the ground, and said unto him, "Why have I found grace in thine eyes, that thou shouldest take knowledge of me, seeing I am a stranger?"

And Boaz answered and said unto her, "It hath fully been shown me, all that thou hast done unto thy mother-in-law since the death of thine husband; and how thou hast left thy father and thy mother, and the land of thy birth, and art come unto a people which thou knewest not heretofore. The Lord recompense thy work, and a full reward be given thee of the Lord God of Israel, under whose wings thou art come to trust."

Then Ruth said, "Let me find favor in thy sight, my lord; for that thou hast comforted me, and for that thou hast spoken friendly unto me, a stranger."

And Boaz said unto her, "At mealtime come thou hither, and eat of the bread, and dip thy morsel in the vinegar."

And she sat beside the reapers; and he reached her parched corn, and she did eat, and was satisfied, and left.

And when she was risen up to glean, Boaz commanded his young men, saying, "Let her glean even among the sheaves, and reproach her not. And let fall also some of the handfuls of purpose for her, and leave them, that she may glean them, and rebuke her not."

So Ruth gleaned in the field until even, and beat out that she had gleaned; and it was about an ephah of barley. And she took it up and went into the city.

And her mother-in-law saw what she had gleaned and said unto her, "Where hast thou gleaned today?" And Ruth said, "The man's name is Boaz."

And Naomi said unto her daughter-in-law, "Blessed be he of the Lord, who hath not left off his kindness to the living and to the dead. The man is near of kin unto us, one of our next kinsmen."

And Ruth the Moabitess said, "He said unto me also, 'Thou shalt keep fast by my young men, until they have ended all my harvest.'"

And Naomi said unto Ruth her daughter-in-law, "It is good, my daughter, that thou go out with his maidens, that they meet thee not in any other field."

So Ruth kept fast by the maidens of Boaz to glean unto the end of the barley harvest and of the wheat harvest, and dwelt with her mother-in-law.

And after the harvest Boaz said unto Ruth, "Blessed be thou of the Lord, my daughter, for thou hast showed more kindness in the latter end than at the beginning. And now all the city of my people doth know that thou art a virtuous woman."

And Boaz loved her, and he took Ruth and she was his wife. And she bore him a son.

Then the women said unto Naomi, "Blessed be the Lord, who hath not left thee this day without a kinsman, that his name may be famous in Israel. And he shall be unto thee a restorer of thy life, and a nourisher of thine old age; for thy daughter-in-law, who loveth thee, who is better to thee than seven sons, hath borne him."

And Naomi took the child, and laid it in her bosom, and became nurse unto it.

And they called the child Obed, and he became the father of Jesse, the father of David.

# Samuel, the Boy Whom God Called

IN THE days when the temple was in the city of Shiloh and Eli and his sons were priests of the Lord, there came to the city to worship a man named Elkanah and his wife Hannah.

Elkanah loved Hannah dearly, but she was unhappy because she had no child. She wept for sorrow and would not eat.

Then said Elkanah her husband, "Hannah, why weepest thou? And why eatest thou not? And why is thy heart grieved? Am I not better to thee than ten sons?"

But Hannah would not be comforted. She fled away to the temple to pray. Eli, the old priest, saw her as she sat by a post in the temple. Weeping bitterly, she prayed that God would give her a son.

"O Lord of hosts," she said, "if Thou wilt remember me and give me a man-child, then will I give him unto the Lord all the days of his life."

She prayed in her heart; only her lips moved; her voice was not heard. Therefore Eli the priest thought she was drunken with wine. And he rebuked her, saying, "How long wilt thou be drunken? Put away thy wine from thee."

And Hannah answered, "No, my lord, I am a woman of sorrowful spirit; I have drunk neither wine nor strong drink, but have poured out my soul before the Lord."

Then she told Eli what troubled her, and he said, "Go in peace, and the God of Israel grant thee thy prayer that thou hast asked of Him."

And it came to pass that Hannah's prayer was answered and a son was born to her. And she called the child Samuel, which means, "asked of the Lord."

Hannah remembered her promise, and as soon as the child was old enough she brought him to the house of the Lord in Shiloh.

She brought the child to Eli and said, "Oh, my lord, as thy soul liveth, I am the woman that stood by thee here, praying unto the Lord. For this child I prayed, and the Lord hath given me my petition which I asked of Him. Therefore also have I lent him to the Lord; as long as he liveth he shall be lent to the Lord."

So saying, she left the child with Eli, the old priest. And Samuel helped Eli in the service of the temple. The child wore a linen ephod, or robe, like that of the priests, and like the priests he ministered unto the Lord. Once each year when she came with her husband to the sacrifice, Hannah brought her son a little coat that she had made.

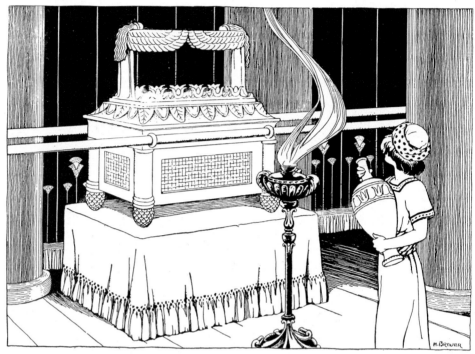

Eli blessed Hannah and Elkanah for having lent Samuel to the Lord and prayed that God might give them other children. And they were blessed with three sons and two daughters.

Thus Samuel grew up in the service of the Lord.

Now Eli's two sons, who were also priests, had not served God as they should have, but had done evil against the people and against the Lord. Eli rebuked them but they hearkened not unto the voice of their father and went on in their evil ways.

Eli was now very old and his eyes were dim. To Samuel was given the task of filling the lamps of the temple with oil and of keeping a light always burning before the ark containing the tables of the Law.

One night when this light was burning dimly and Samuel had gone to rest, he heard a voice call, "Samuel!"

He ran at once to Eli, saying, "Here am I, for thou didst call me."

"I called thee not," said Eli. "Lie down again."

So Samuel lay down again, but scarcely had he done so, when he heard the voice again, "Samuel, Samuel!"

Again he ran to Eli, and again Eli said, "I called not, my son; lie down again."

When the voice called a third time and Samuel went to Eli as before, the old priest knew that it must be the Lord who had called the child. So he said to the boy, "Lie down and it shall be, if He call thee, thou shalt answer, 'Speak, Lord, for Thy servant heareth.'"

Samuel lay down again and presently he heard the voice call, "Samuel, Samuel." And he answered, "Speak, Lord, for Thy servant heareth."

Then God told Samuel that because Eli's sons had done evil and Eli had not turned them away from their wickedness, He would bring punishment upon the priest's whole family and would destroy them all.

Samuel lay in his bed until morning. He feared to tell Eli what God had told him.

But Eli called him and said, "Samuel, my son," and he answered, "Here am I."

"What is it that the Lord hath said unto thee? I pray thee hide it not from me."

Then Samuel told Eli all that had passed and hid nothing from him.

And Eli said to Samuel, "It is the Lord; let Him do what seemeth Him good."

In time all came to pass as had been foretold. Eli's two sons were both killed in battle on the same day. And Eli himself died of shock and grief.

Meanwhile Samuel grew and the Lord was with him. And he became known throughout all the land as a prophet of the Lord.

# Joseph and His Brothers

### THE DREAMER

JACOB was an old man and lived in Hebron, in the land of Canaan. The Lord had dealt graciously with Jacob, and had prospered his flocks and his herds, but of all his riches he was most blessed in his twelve sons. They were all well pleasing to their father, but Jacob loved Joseph more than all his other children, because he was the son of his old age, and Jacob made for this well-loved son a coat of many colors. And when the brothers saw that their father loved him more than he loved them, they hated Joseph.

Now, Joseph dreamed a dream, and he told it to his brothers: "Hear, I pray you, this dream which I have dreamed. For, behold, we were binding sheaves in the field, and lo, my sheaf arose and stood upright, and behold, your sheaves stood round about, and bowed down to my sheaf."

Great anger came upon his brothers when they heard this dream, and they cried out upon him, saying, "Shalt thou, indeed, rule over us?" and they hated him the more for his dream.

Then Joseph dreamed another dream, and told it to his brothers, saying, "Behold, I have dreamed yet another dream, and behold, the sun, the moon, and the eleven stars bowed down to me." And he told this dream to his father and to his brothers.

His father rebuked him, saying, "Shall I and thy mother and thy brothers, indeed, come to bow down ourselves to thee to the earth?" And yet Jacob marked well this second dream of Joseph, his son, while the brothers hated and envied the lad still more.

JOSEPH SOLD INTO SLAVERY

Now it came to pass that the brothers went to feed their father's flock in Shechem, and Jacob said unto Joseph, his son, "Go, I pray thee, and find thy brothers. See whether it be well with them, and with the flocks, and bring me word again."

And Joseph answered, "Here am I," and set off at once.

Now the brothers saw him coming while he was yet afar off, and they plotted together to kill him, and said one to another, "Behold, this dreamer cometh; he who saith that we shall all bow down to him! Come, therefore, let us kill him and throw him into some pit. Then will we tell our father that wild beasts did devour him— and we shall see what will become of his dreams."

But one brother, Reuben by name, said, "Let us not kill him; let us shed no blood. Instead, let us throw him into a pit and there leave him." This said Reuben, thinking to save Joseph from them, and then to bring him from the pit, and take him home to his father. The brothers were persuaded to do this thing, and Reuben left them for a time.

So when Joseph came unto his brothers, they took off his coat of many colors and threw him into an empty pit. Then they sat down to eat bread. But while they ate, lo, a company of Ishmaelites came down from Gilead with their camels, bearing spicery, balm, and myrrh to Egypt.

And Judah, another of the brothers, said, "What profit is it if we kill our brother and hide his blood? Come, let us sell him to the Ishmaelites, and let not our hand be upon him, for he is our brother and our flesh."

And his brothers were content. They drew Joseph out of the pit, and sold him to the Ishmaelites for twenty pieces of silver, and the caravan of the Ishmaelites bore Joseph out of the land of his brothers, down into Egypt.

Then returned Reuben unto the brothers, and seeing that Joseph was not in the pit, said unto them, "Where now have ye put Joseph, our brother?"

When they told him they had sold Joseph for a slave unto the Ishmaelites, Reuben tore his clothes and wept, saying, "The child is not here, and I, whither shall I go?"

The brothers took Joseph's coat of many colors and dipped it in the blood of an animal they had killed. Then they bore it to Jacob, their father, saying, "This coat, stained with blood, have we found; tell us, is it thy son's coat?"

When Jacob saw the coat he had made for Joseph, all covered over with blood, he cried in a loud voice, "It is, indeed, the coat of Joseph, my son. An evil beast hath devoured him. Without doubt, Joseph hath been killed!"

Then the aged Jacob tore his clothes with grief, and mourned for his son many days. All his sons and all his daughters rose up to comfort him, but he refused to be comforted, and he said, "I will go down into my grave mourning for my son Joseph!" Thus his father wept for him.

JOSEPH IN EGYPT

Joseph was brought down into Egypt by the Ishmaelites. There Potiphar, an officer of Pharaoh, the King, bought Joseph for a slave. And the Lord was with Joseph, and he prospered. Potiphar made him overseer over his house. But it came to pass that Joseph was falsely accused of wrongdoing. Because of this, he was thrown into prison, where the King's prisoners were bound.

Here, also, the Lord was with Joseph, and the keeper of the prison showed favor unto Joseph, and made him head of all his work.

Now, it came to pass that Pharaoh's butler and his baker offended their King, and were thrown into that same prison where Joseph was.

One night they dreamed a dream, both of them, and the next day when Joseph came upon them, behold, they were sad, and he said unto them, "Wherefore look ye so sad today?"

They answered each of them, "We have dreamed a dream this night, and there is no one to tell us what the dream means."

"The meaning of a dream is with God," said Joseph. "Tell me, then, your dream, for it may be that God will give me to know the meaning of it."

The chief butler of Pharaoh told his dream, saying, "In my dream, behold, a vine was before me, with three branches. As I looked, it began to bud and blossom, and the clusters thereof brought forth ripe grapes. I took the grapes, and I pressed the juice of them into Pharaoh's cup, and I gave the cup into Pharaoh's own hand."

Then answered Joseph, "This is the meaning of thy dream. The

three branches are three days. Within three days Pharaoh, the King, shall restore thee to thy place in his household. Thou shalt once more bear Pharaoh's cup unto him and serve him in thy former manner. When it is thus well with thee, think on me, I pray thee. For indeed I was stolen away out of the land of the Hebrews, and here also have I done nothing that they should put me into the dungeon."

The chief baker of the King heard all this, and when he heard that the meaning of the butler's dream was good, he said unto Joseph, "Hear now, this dream of mine, and tell me what is the meaning of it. In my dream, behold, I had three white baskets on my head. In the uppermost basket there were all kinds of bake-meats for Pharaoh, and the birds did eat out of this basket."

Joseph answered, "This is the meaning of thy dream. The three baskets are three days. Within three days shall Pharaoh hang thee on a tree, and the birds shall eat thy flesh."

It came to pass just as Joseph had said. Pharaoh restored his chief butler to his place, but the chief baker was hanged.

PHARAOH DREAMS A DREAM

It came to pass, at the end of two years, that Pharaoh, the King, dreamed a dream which none could explain. Then he slept and dreamed a second time, and in the morning his spirit was troubled. He sent for all the magicians of Egypt, and all the wise men thereof, but there was none of them that could explain his dream.

Then spake the chief butler unto the King, "Now I do remember my faults. In prison there is a youth whom I promised not to forget. He it is who is most skillful in telling the meaning of dreams."

Then Pharaoh sent and called for Joseph, and they brought him hastily out of the dungeon.

And Pharaoh said unto Joseph, "I have heard say of thee that thou canst explain a dream."

And Joseph answered, "The meaning lies not with me, but with God. Tell me thy dream, that God may give thee an answer to it."

And Pharaoh said, "In my dream, behold, I stood by the bank of a river, and there came up out of the river seven cows, fat and well-favored, and they fed in a meadow. After them came seven other

cows, lean and ill-favored.   And the lean cows did eat up the fat
cows.   And when they had eaten them they were still ill-favored as
at the beginning.   So I awoke.

"Then, I dreamed again, and in my dream I saw seven ears come
up on one stalk, full and good.   Then sprang up seven withered ears,
thin and blasted, and the seven thin ears devoured the seven fat ears.
I have told these dreams unto our magicians, but none can tell the
meaning unto me."

And Joseph said unto Pharaoh, "Thy two dreams are one.   God
hath showed Pharaoh what He is about to do.   The seven good cows
and the seven good ears are the seven years of plenty which Egypt
is to have.   And the seven lean cows and the seven withered ears
are the seven years of famine which will follow.   During the seven
lean years all the plenty shall be consumed in the land of Egypt, and
the famine shall be very grievous.   God will shortly bring this to
pass; prepare now as God hath warned thee.   Find a man discreet
and wise and set him over the land of Egypt.   Let him appoint
officers to take up one-fifth part of the crops in the seven plenteous
years.   Let the food be kept in great storehouses in the cities, against
the time when the famine shall come; then only shall Egypt not
perish when the lean years come."

Then said Pharaoh unto Joseph, "God hath given thee great wisdom.   There is none so discreet and wise as thou art.   I shall set
thee over the land of Egypt, and according to thy word shall all my
people be ruled."

Pharaoh then took a ring off his finger, and put it upon Joseph's
hand, and clothed him in fine linen and put a gold chain about his
neck.   Then Pharaoh cried, "Bow the knee!" and the people bowed
before Joseph as before the King, and Joseph rode in a chariot next
to the King.

Joseph went out from the presence of Pharaoh and went throughout all the land of Egypt. During the seven years of plenty Joseph harvested the crops, saving one-fifth part to be stored. And Joseph gathered corn as the sand of the sea, till it was past all numbering.

Then the seven years of famine began, even as Joseph had said, and the famine was in all the lands round about. Only in Egypt was there plenty, because of Joseph's wisdom.

Then, when the people cried to the King for bread, he answered them, "Go unto Joseph. What he tells you to do, do it."

And all the neighboring countries began to come into Egypt to buy corn of Joseph.

THE BROTHERS BOW DOWN TO JOSEPH

Now the famine was in the land of the Hebrews, and Jacob said unto his sons, "Behold, I have heard that there is food in Egypt. Get you down and buy corn for us, that we may not die. But take not Benjamin, your youngest brother, with you, he that is own brother to my lost son Joseph. Let Benjamin rest at home, lest some mischief befall him."

The brothers came to Egypt unto Joseph, who was the governor of the land, and they knew him not. They bowed themselves before him, with their faces to the earth. And Joseph saw his brothers and knew them, but he saw that they knew not him, so he made himself rough to them, and he said, "Whence come ye?"

"From Canaan, the land of the Hebrews, to buy corn," they answered, and again they bowed before him.

And Joseph remembered his dream of the brothers bowing before him, and he said, "Ye are spies. Ye come not for corn, but to spy on the land of Egypt."

And they said, "Nay, nay, my lord, we are true men and no spies. Thy servants are twelve brothers, the sons of one man in the land of Canaan, and behold, the youngest is this day with our father, and one is not."

"If ye be not spies," answered Joseph, "bring your youngest brother unto me. Let one of you remain here in prison until your return. Go ye, carry back corn to your families, but unless ye return with your brother, ye shall surely die."

Then the brothers said to one another, "It is because of our sin against Joseph, our brother, that this has come upon us," and Reuben added, "Spake I not unto you, telling you to sin not against the child? Now Benjamin must suffer for the evil we have done."

And they knew not that Joseph understood them, but when the brothers saw him not, he turned aside and wept.

Joseph took Simeon, one of the brothers, and bound him before their eyes. Then Joseph commanded his servants to fill the brothers' sacks with corn and to put every man's money back into his sack.

When the brothers came unto the house of Jacob, their father, and opened every man his sack, lo, the money was within. Then were the brothers afraid, and they told Jacob all that had happened to them in the land of Egypt.

Jacob cried out against them, "Ye have bereaved me of my children. Joseph is not, and Simeon is not, and now ye will take Benjamin away. All things are against me. Benjamin shall not go down into Egypt. If anything should happen to him there, it would bring down my gray hairs in sorrow to the grave."

But time passed, and the famine continued. At last there was no more food in Canaan, and Jacob knew that they must go once more to the great ruler in Egypt; so he called the brothers together, and he placed Benjamin in their midst, saying,

"If it must be so now, do this: carry down to the man a little present—a little balm, a little honey, spices and myrrh, nuts and almonds. Take also double money in your hand. Go unto this man with your brother Benjamin, and God Almighty give you mercy before this man, that he may let your brother go in safety. If I am bereaved of my children, I am bereaved!"

JOSEPH REVEALS HIMSELF TO HIS BROTHERS

Now when the brothers were come again before Joseph's door, they were told that on that day at noon they were to eat with Joseph. They made ready their present, as their father had commanded, and at noon they stood before Joseph, and he said,

"Is your father well, the old man of whom ye spake? Is he yet alive?"

They answered, "Thy servant, our father, is in good health," and they bowed down their heads to him.

Joseph lifted up his eyes, and saw his brother, Benjamin, his mother's son, and he asked, "Is this your younger brother of whom ye spake unto me?" And he said, "God be gracious unto thee, my son."

And Joseph was greatly moved, and went into the next room and wept. When he returned, he had food set before them, and they wondered greatly, for the food that was set before Benjamin was always much more than that which was set before them.

While they ate, Joseph commanded his steward, saying, "Fill

their sacks with grain, all they can carry, and put every man's money in his sack. But in the sack of the youngest put my silver cup." And the man did as Joseph told him.

As soon as the next day was come, the brothers started on their way with their sacks of corn, but they had not gone far, when the steward overtook them, crying out, "Wherefore have ye rewarded evil for good? Hath not my master given you to eat and to drink, that ye must needs steal the silver cup which he useth?"

The brothers said, "God forbid that thy servants should do such a thing. Search now our sacks, we pray thee, that thou mayest see for thyself that the cup is not with us. With whomsoever of thy servants it be found, let that one die, and we will be forever bondmen to thy master."

Then every man opened his sack, and lo, in the sack of Benjamin the silver cup was found. Then the brothers tore their clothes, and returned in haste to the house of Joseph.

They fell on their faces before him, and Judah said, "What shall we say unto my lord, and what shall we cry out; how shall we clear ourselves, and what shall we speak? Benjamin, our brother, took not thy cup, but how shall we tell that unto thee, when it was found with him?" And the brothers wept.

And Judah said, "Lord, we told thee of our father, how he is an old man. He loved Joseph, his son, more than any of us, but Joseph is no more. Then did our father turn his heart towards Benjamin, the brother of Joseph, son of the same mother. If we return not to Jacob, our father, with this lad, his heart will break, and he will die. We cannot go down to him. If our youngest brother be not with us, we may not see our father's face. I pray thee let me take Benjamin's place. Let me die, or let me be thy bondman and thy slave all the days of my life; only let Benjamin, I pray thee, return to my father."

When Joseph heard this, he cried, "Let every man go out from me, save only these brothers."

Then when Joseph stood alone with his brothers, he made himself known unto them, saying, "Do ye know me not? I am Joseph, your brother."

They were deeply troubled at his words, and remembered how they had sold him for a slave into Egypt.

And Joseph saw their sorrow, and said unto them, "Be not grieved nor angry with yourselves because ye sold me hither. God did send me before you into Egypt to save your lives. For only two years hath the famine consumed the land, and yet there are five more years when there shall be no harvest. But I have great storehouses, with plenty for all. So, it was not you that sent me hither, but God. Now ye must go to Jacob, our father, and tell him of all that hath come to pass. Tell my father of my glory in Egypt, and bring him hither in all haste."

Then Joseph fell upon the neck of Benjamin, his brother, and wept, and Benjamin wept also. After that, Joseph embraced his brothers, and forgave them all that they had done unto him. Then, the brothers returned to Canaan to their father Jacob, and told him all that had come to pass. His heart leaped with joy, and he journeyed down into the land of Egypt to abide with Joseph, his son, and with all of his sons, so long as he lived.

## David and Goliath

THERE was an old man in Bethlehem, called Jesse, who had eight sons, and the youngest of these sons was called David. There was war between the Israelites and the Philistines, and Saul, the king of Israel, gathered his army against the enemy. Jesse's older sons followed Saul to war, but David, who was but a lad, remained at home, to feed his father's sheep.

One day Jesse called David unto him, and said, "Go now, to Saul's camp, and take this parched corn, and these ten loaves, and run to the camp of thy brothers quickly. Take, also, these ten cheeses unto the captain of their thousand, and see how thy brothers fare, and bring me word of them."

So David rose up early in the morning, and left the sheep with a keeper, and set off, as Jesse had commanded him, to find his brothers in Saul's camp.

David found the army in battle array, drawn up on the top of a hill, facing the Philistines. And while he and his brothers talked together, there came up from among the Philistines a great giant, Goliath by name. He had a helmet of brass upon his head, and he was armed with a coat of mail. He had greaves of brass upon his legs, and a target of brass between his shoulders. His spear was like a weaver's beam, and one went before him, bearing his shield.

And he stood and cried out to the army of Israel, saying, "Why are ye come out to set your battle in array? Am I not a Philistine, and ye the servants of Saul? Let us put away now our armies, and instead, choose you a man for you, and let him come down and fight with me. If he be able to kill me, then will we be your servants, but if I prevail against him, then must ye be our servants."

And all the men of Israel, when they saw the man, fled from him, and were sore afraid.

And the men of Israel said, "Have ye seen this man that is come up? Surely it is to defy Israel that he is come up. No man have we who dares to go out against him, and yet, the King hath promised to enrich greatly the man who killeth this giant, and to give him his daughter in marriage."

"Then why goeth not some man from among you to slay this Philistine?" asked David.

His brothers were angry with him, that he should speak so, and Eliab, the eldest brother, cried out against him, saying, "Why camest thou down hither, and with whom hast thou left our father's sheep? I know thy pride and the naughtiness which is in thy heart, for thou art come down that thou mightest see the battle."

And David answered, "What have I now done? Is there not a cause? I would fight this Philistine gladly, if the King would but have me."

When these words were heard which David spoke, the men carried them quickly to the King, and Saul sent for David.

When he stood before the King, David said, "Let no man's heart fail because of Goliath. Thy servant will go, even now, and fight with this Philistine."

But when Saul's eyes fell upon David, he said, "Thou art not able to go against this Philistine to fight with him. Why, thou art but a youth, and he is a man of war."

Then David said unto Saul, "Thy servant kept his father's sheep, and there came a lion, and a bear, and took a lamb out of the flock. And I went out after him, and smote him and delivered it out of his mouth. And when he rose up against me, I caught him by his beard and smote him and slew him. Thy servant slew the lion and the bear. And this Philistine shall be as the lion or the bear, for he hath defied the armies of the living God, and I will slay him. The Lord hath delivered me out of the paw of the lion and of the bear; He will deliver me also out of the hand of this Philistine."

Now Saul was glad within him when he heard these words that David spake, and he said unto him, "Go, and the Lord be with thee."

And Saul armed David with his armor. He put a helmet of brass upon his head, and he armed him with a coat of mail. And David put on the King's sword and tried to go forth, but it felt strange to him and he liked not the newness of it, and he said unto the King, "I cannot wear thy armor, for I have not proved it. As I came to thy camp, so will I go against this Goliath."

Then David took his staff in his hand and his sling also. He chose five smooth stones from out of the brook, and put them in his shepherd's bag, which he had with him, and he drew near to the Philistine.

Now the Philistine, Goliath, came before him all in shining armor, and one walked before him bearing his shield.

When the giant looked about him and saw only a shepherd lad, young, ruddy, and of a fair countenance, he cried, "Am I a dog that thou comest against me with sticks and stones? Come to me, and I will give thy flesh unto the fowls of the air and thy body to the beasts of the field."

Then answered David, "Thou comest to me armed with a sword, and with a spear, and with a shield, but I come to thee in the name of the Lord of hosts, the God of the armies of Israel whom thou hast defied. This day will the Lord deliver thee into mine hand, and I will smite thee, that all the earth may know that there is a God in Israel. And all shall know that the Lord saveth not with sword and spear, for the battle is the Lord's."

Then the Philistine rose and drew near unto David, to kill him with his mighty sword. And David ran towards him to meet him, and as he ran he put his hand in his bag and took thence a stone, and put it in his sling and hurled it at Goliath. This pebble from the brook smote the Philistine in the forehead, and sank into his forehead, and he fell upon his face to the earth. Then David took the sword of Goliath and slew him and cut off his head. And when the Philistines saw their champion was dead, they all fled.

## David and Jonathan

AFTER David had slain the giant Goliath, he was brought before King Saul. And Saul said to him, "Whose son art thou, thou young man?"

And David answered, "I am the son of thy servant Jesse, the Bethlehemite."

Beside the King was his son Jonathan, and, as David spoke these words, the soul of Jonathan was knit with the soul of David, and Jonathan loved David as his own soul.

And Saul kept David with him and would let him go no more home to his father's house. Jonathan and David made a promise that they would always be friends. And, as a sign of this, Jonathan took off his princely robe and placed it upon David, and he took his sword and his bow and his girdle and gave them all to David.

David went out whither Saul sent him, and behaved himself wisely. And Saul set him over the men of war.

And now it came to pass when David was returned from battle with the Philistines that the women came out dancing and singing a song of victory, and they said, "Saul hath slain his thousands, and David his ten thousands."

Then Saul was angry and he said, "They have ascribed unto David ten thousands, and to me they have ascribed but thousands: and what can he have more but the kingdom?"

And it came to pass on the morrow that an evil spirit came upon

Saul. And when David came before him to play his harp as at other times, Saul in his anger cast a javelin at David, and he was forced to flee from the King's presence.

Saul was afraid of David, because the Lord was with him, and was departed from Saul. Therefore he removed David from him and made him his captain over a thousand men, and sent him out to battle against the Philistines. For he thought to make David fall by the hand of the Philistines.

But when David won against the Philistines, Saul was yet the more afraid of David, and Saul hated David more and more.

And Saul spake to Jonathan his son, and to all his servants, that they should kill David.

But Jonathan delighted much in David, and he told David, saying, "Saul my father seeketh to kill thee: now therefore, I pray thee, take heed to thyself until the morning, and abide in a secret place, and hide thyself. And I will go out and stand beside my father in the field where thou art, and I will speak with my father of thee, and what I see that will I tell thee."

And Jonathan spake good of David unto Saul his father, and said unto him, "Let not the King sin against his servant, against David, because he hath not sinned against thee, but hath done well toward thee. For he did put his life in his hand, and slew the Philistine, and the Lord saved all Israel. Thou sawest it and didst rejoice. Wherefore, then, wilt thou sin against innocent blood, to slay David without cause?"

And Saul hearkened unto the words of Jonathan and promised, "As the Lord liveth, he shall not be slain."

Jonathan called David and told him all this. And Jonathan brought David to Saul, and he was with him as in times past.

Then there was war again, and David went out and fought and won against the Philistines, and they fled from him.

Again the evil spirit was upon Saul. And David played for him as before. And again Saul tried to strike David with his javelin, but David slipped away and escaped.

Saul also sent messengers unto David's house to watch him and to slay him in the morning, but David escaped through a window and fled away. Saul sent messengers to follow and take David, and David fled from place to place.

At length David came to Jonathan and said, "What have I done, and what is my sin before thy father, that he seeketh my life?"

And Jonathan said, "God forbid; thou shalt not die. Behold my father will do nothing either great or small but that he will show it to me. And why should my father hide this thing from me? It is not so."

But David said, "Thy father certainly knoweth that I am a close friend to thee. And he saith, 'Let not Jonathan know this, lest he be grieved.' But truly as the Lord liveth, and as thy soul liveth, there is but a step between me and death."

Then said Jonathan unto David, "Whatsoever thy soul desireth, I will even do it for thee."

And David said unto Jonathan, "Behold, tomorrow is the new moon, and I should not fail to sit with the King at meat, but let me go that I may hide myself in the field unto the third day at even. If thy father at all miss me, then say, 'David earnestly asked leave of me that he might run to Bethlehem, his city, for there is a yearly sacrifice there for all the family.' If he say thus, 'It is well,' thy servant shall have peace, but if he be very angry, then be sure that he plans evil against me.

"Thou hast made a bond of friendship with me before the Lord," said David, "yet if there be in me any guilt, slay me thyself, for why shouldst thou bring me to thy father?"

And Jonathan said, "Far be it from thee, for if I knew certainly that my father meant to bring evil upon thee, then would I not tell thee?"

Then said David to Jonathan, "Who shall tell me? Or what if thy father answer thee roughly?"

And Jonathan said unto David, "Come, let us go out into the field."

And they went out both of them into the field, and Jonathan made a solemn promise, saying, "O Lord God of Israel, when I have sounded my father, and, behold, if there be good toward David, and I then send not unto thee, and show it thee, the Lord do so and much more to Jonathan. But if it please my father to do thee evil, then I will show it thee, and send thee away, that thou mayest go in peace; and the Lord be with thee, as he hath been with my father." So Jonathan renewed his promise of friendship with David, because he loved him as he loved his own soul.

Then Jonathan said to David, "Tomorrow is the new moon, and thou shalt be missed, because thy seat will be empty. And when thou hast stayed three days, then shalt thou go down to the place where thou didst hide thyself before. And I will shoot three arrows on the side thereof, as though I shot at a mark. And, behold, I will send a lad, saying, 'Go, find out the arrows.' If I expressly say unto the lad, 'Behold the arrows are on this side of thee, take them,' then come thou, for there is peace to thee, and no hurt, as the Lord liveth. But if I say thus unto the young man, 'Behold, the arrows are beyond thee,' go thy way, for the Lord hath sent thee away."

So David hid himself in the field. And when the new moon was come, and the King sat him down to eat meat, David's place was empty. Nevertheless Saul spake not anything that day, for he thought, "Something hath befallen him."

But it came to pass on the second day when David's place was empty, Saul said unto Jonathan his son, "Wherefore cometh not the son of Jesse to meat, neither yesterday nor today?"

And Jonathan answered, "David earnestly asked leave of me to go to Bethlehem, for he said, 'Our family hath a sacrifice in the city.' Therefore he cometh not unto the King's table."

Then Saul's anger was kindled against Jonathan, and he said unto him, "Thou son of the perverse rebellious woman, do not I know that thou hast chosen the son of Jesse to thine own harm? For as long as he liveth, thou shalt not be safe, nor thy kingdom. Wherefore now send and fetch him unto me, for he shall surely die."

And Jonathan answered Saul, his father, and said unto him, "Wherefore shall he be slain? What hath he done?"

And Saul cast a javelin at him to strike him. So Jonathan knew that his father meant to slay David. And he arose from the table in fierce anger, and did eat no meat, for he was grieved for David, because his father had done him shame.

In the morning Jonathan went out into the field at the time appointed with David, and a little lad with him. And he said unto his lad, "Run, find out now the arrows which I shoot." And as the lad ran he shot an arrow beyond him.

And when the lad was come to the place of the arrow which Jonathan had shot, Jonathan cried after the lad, and said, "Is not the arrow beyond thee? Make speed, haste, stay not."

And Jonathan's lad gathered up the arrows and came to his master. But the lad knew not anything: only Jonathan and David knew the matter.

And Jonathan bade the lad return to the city.

And as soon as the lad was gone, David arose out of a place toward the south, and fell on his face to the ground, and bowed himself three times. And they kissed one another, and wept with one another.

And Jonathan said to David, "Go in peace, forasmuch as we have sworn both of us in the name of the Lord, saying, 'The Lord be between me and thee, and between my seed and thy seed forever.'" And so they parted.

# Prayers for Every Day

DEAR LORD, for these three things I pray:
To know Thee more clearly,
To love Thee more dearly,
To follow Thee more nearly,
Every day.

GOD is Love;
God is Good;
And we thank Him
For our food.

FATHER of all, in Heaven above,
We thank Thee for Thy love;
Our food, our home, and all we wear
Tell of Thy loving care.

FATHER, we thank Thee for the night,
And for the pleasant morning light;
For rest and food and loving care,
And all that makes the day so fair.

Help us to do the things we should,
To be to others kind and good;
In all we do in work or play,
To grow more loving every day.

FATHER of all, we thank Thee for this day. Help us to meet it with joy, and to do with courage and gladness all those tasks which a good day brings. Help us to feel Thy love and strength supporting us, and to know that with Thee all things are possible.

# The Nineteenth Psalm

THE heavens declare the glory of God;
And the firmament sheweth his handywork.
Day unto day uttereth speech,
And night unto night sheweth knowledge.
There is no speech nor language,
Where their voice is not heard.
Their line is gone out through all the earth,
And their words to the end of the world.
In them hath he set a tabernacle for the sun,
Which is as a bridegroom coming out of his chamber,
And rejoiceth as a strong man to run a race.
His going forth is from the end of the heaven,
And his circuit unto the ends of it:
And there is nothing hid from the heat thereof.
The law of the Lord is perfect, converting the soul:
The testimony of the Lord is sure, making wise the simple.
The statutes of the Lord are right, rejoicing the heart:
The commandment of the Lord is pure, enlightening the eyes.

The fear of the Lord is clean, enduring for ever:
The judgments of the Lord are true and righteous altogether.
More to be desired are they than gold, yea, than much fine
    gold:
Sweeter also than honey and the honeycomb.
Moreover by them is thy servant warned:
And in keeping of them there is great reward.
Who can understand his errors?
Cleanse thou me from secret faults.
Keep back thy servant also from presumptuous sins;
Let them not have dominion over me:
Then shall I be upright,
And I shall be innocent from the great transgression.
Let the words of my mouth,
And the meditation of my heart, be acceptable in thy sight,
O Lord, my strength, and my redeemer.

# The Twenty-fourth Psalm

THE earth is the Lord's, and the fulness thereof;
The world, and they that dwell therein.
For he hath founded it upon the seas,
And established it upon the floods.
Who shall ascend into the hill of the Lord?
Or who shall stand in his holy place?
He that hath clean hands, and a pure heart;
Who hath not lifted up his soul unto vanity,
Nor sworn deceitfully.
He shall receive the blessing from the Lord,
And righteousness from the God of his salvation.
This is the generation of them that seek him,
That seek thy face, O Jacob.
Lift up your heads, O ye gates;
And be ye lift up, ye everlasting doors;
And the King of glory shall come in.
Who is this King of glory?
The Lord strong and mighty,
The Lord mighty in battle.
Lift up your heads, O ye gates;
Even lift them up, ye everlasting doors;
And the King of glory shall come in.
Who is this King of glory?
The Lord of hosts, he is the King of glory.

# The One Hundred and Twenty-first Psalm

I WILL lift up mine eyes unto the hills,
From whence cometh my help.
My help cometh from the Lord,
Which made heaven and earth.
He will not suffer thy foot to be moved:
He that keepeth thee will not slumber.
Behold, he that keepeth Israel
Shall neither slumber nor sleep.
The Lord is thy keeper:
The Lord is thy shade upon thy right hand.
The sun shall not smite thee by day,
Nor the moon by night.
The Lord shall preserve thee from all evil:
He shall preserve thy soul.
The Lord shall preserve thy going out and thy coming in
From this time forth, and even for evermore.

# Jesus of Nazareth

## THE SHEPHERDS

AND it came to pass in those days that an order was sent out by the great emperor Caesar Augustus that all the people in the Roman world were to be counted. And everyone was to go to his own city. Joseph, with his wife Mary, also went up from Galilee out of the city of Nazareth to the city of David, which is called Bethlehem, because he was of the family of David. And it came to pass that while they were there that Mary's Son was born, and she laid Him in a manger because there was no room for them in the inn.

And there were in the same country shepherds keeping watch over their flocks by night. And behold, an angel of the Lord came to them and the glory of the Lord shone round about them, and they feared with a great fear. And the angel said to them: "Fear not! For, behold, I bring you good tidings of great joy which shall be for all people. For unto you is born this day in the city of David a Savior who is Christ, the Lord. And this shall be a sign to you: You shall find the Child wrapped in swaddling clothes and lying in a manger."

And suddenly there was with the angel a multitude of the heavenly host, praising God and saying: "Glory to God in the highest, and peace on earth among men of good will."

And it came to pass after the angels departed from them into heaven, the shepherds said to one another, "Let us go over to Bethlehem and see what the Lord has promised us." And they came quickly and found Mary and Joseph and the Child lying in the manger. And the shepherds returned, glorifying and praising God for all the things they had heard and seen.

### THE WISE MEN

When Jesus was born in Bethlehem of Judea in the days of Herod the King, behold, wise men came from the East to Jerusalem saying, "Where is He that is born king, for we have seen His star in the east and have come to worship Him?"

And King Herod, when he heard this, was troubled and all Jerusalem with him. And assembling together all the chief priests and the scribes of the people, he inquired of them where Christ was to be born. And they told him, "In Bethlehem of Judea."

Then Herod, calling together the wise men, learned from them the time when the star appeared. And sending them into Bethlehem, he said, "Go and search for the Child, and when you have found Him, bring me word again that I also may come and worship Him." They, having heard the king, went their way. And behold, the star, which they had seen in their own countries, went before them until it came and stood over the place where the young Child lay. And seeing the star they rejoiced with exceeding great joy. And entering into the house they found the Child with Mary, His mother, and falling down, they worshipped Him. And opening their treasures, they offered Him gifts, gold, and frankincense, and myrrh. And having been warned by

God in a dream that they were not to return to Herod, they went back to their own country another way.

### JESUS IN THE TEMPLE

And every year His father and mother went to Jerusalem at the time of the great Jewish feast of Passover. And when He was twelve years old, they went up as they always did to the feast. And when the days of the feast were over and they were returning to their own town, the boy Jesus remained in Jerusalem. His parents did not know this, for they thought He was in the great company of people who had journeyed to the feast with them. They had come a day's journey before they began to seek Him among their relatives and their friends. And when they could not find Him, they returned to Jerusalem.

And it came to pass that, after three days, they found Him in the temple, sitting in the midst of the learned men, hearing them and asking them questions. And all to whose ears it came were full of wonder at His knowledge and the answers which He gave. And when His parents saw Him, they too were amazed, and His mother said to Him, "Son, why did you do this to us? Your father and I have sought for you with sorrow." And He said to them, "Why did you seek for me? Did you not know that I must be about my Father's business?" And they did not understand the words He spoke to them. And He returned with them to their own city of Nazareth in Galilee, and did everything His parents asked. And His mother kept all these words in her heart. And Jesus increased in wisdom and in years, and in grace before God and men.

### THE DAUGHTER OF JAIRUS

While Jesus was preaching at Capernaum by the sea of Galilee, a great crowd came out to hear Him. And a ruler named Jairus, when he saw Jesus, fell at His feet and pleaded with Him, saying, "My daughter lies at the point of death. Come and lay your hands on her that she may be healed and live."

And Jesus went with him and many people thronged about Him. Then came someone from the house of the ruler, saying, "Your daughter is dead. Why do you trouble the Master further?" But Jesus said to the ruler, "Do not be afraid, only have faith." And He allowed no one to follow Him except His disciples, Peter and James and John.

And He came to the house of the ruler and, seeing the people weeping and wailing, He said to them, "Why do you make this din? Why do you weep? The girl is asleep, not dead." And they laughed Him to scorn. But when He had put them all out, He took the father and the mother and the three disciples with Him and entered the room where the little girl was lying.

And He took her by the hand and said to her, "Child, I say to you, arise!" And the girl rose up immediately and began to walk about; and she was twelve years old. And they were utterly amazed. And He charged them strictly that they should tell no man of what He had done, but His fame spread abroad throughout all that land.

# INDEX OF AUTHORS

[This index is for Volumes Three, Four, Five, and Six. The index for Volumes One and Two appears in the back of Volume Two. This index includes some stories retold or adapted.]

INDEX OF TITLES

[This index is for Volumes Three, Four, Five, and Six. The index for Volumes One and Two appears in the back of Volume Two.]